BRUNEL: Engineering Giant

'Engineers are extremely necessary for these
purposes; wherefore it is requisite that, besides being
ingenious, they should be brave in proportion.'
– *Nicholson's British Encyclopedia* 1809

BRUNEL:
Engineering Giant

Peter Hay

B.T. Batsford Ltd, London

For Teresa

First paperback edition 1985

Originally published under the title
Brunel: his achievements in the transport revolution
in 1973 by Osprey Publishing Ltd.

© Peter Hay 1973

ISBN 0 7134 5172 6

Printed in Great Britain by
Billing Ltd, Worcester
for the publishers,
B.T. Batsford Ltd
4 Fitzhardinge Street
London
W1H 0AH

Preface

As I myself never read authors' prefaces, I cannot complain if nobody reads this one. For those of greater virtue, however, some small explanation. Fashions change in history as in everything else, but although history through biography is no longer new, I hope those who read this book will find it adds a little to their knowledge of the history of the period, as well as to their knowledge of Brunel and what he did. Most of his achievements are recorded here, and those left out do not, in my opinion, add to our understanding of Brunel as an innovator. Of his major exploits, probably his work on steamships is his best claim to the description. In this context, the accusation that he constantly pursued novelty for its own sake must here be denied. His aim was rather always to find a better way of doing whatever he was trying to do, and by that test, the atmospheric system was his major failure.

I hope also that this book will do something to kill the myth that Brunel was a man to whom expense was never allowed to stand in the way of success for his ideas. In sober truth, many of them were aimed at saving expense, and money troubles often came not because of his original plans, but from failure to carry them out.

He lived at a time of rapidly accelerating change and in an age of giants, and in every sense he was a man of his times.

Acknowledgements

Some people help authors. Others, harder pressed and therefore the more to be thanked, have to put up with them as well. This has been the fate of Miss Baird and her staff at Brighton Reference Library, and of those who guard the archives of the British Railways Board. I must also acknowledge my debt to Ray Watkinson, and to those who have previously written about Isambard Brunel, especially his son – whose book is, happily, now reprinted – and L. T. C. Rolt, in whose works I have found a mine of information. Extensive use has also been made of the papers of Parliament, and of the letter-books and other personal records deposited by the Brunel family with the University of Bristol. I am greatly indebted to Mr. Maby of that city for his patience. In writing this book, I join the ranks of the many whose researches would have been less complete and very much the poorer without the efforts of those unknown chroniclers of *The Times* newspaper from whose labours has so often come light in the darkness, and I am happy to render my thanks to them here. The sources of the illustrations are given underneath each picture.

Contents

Illustrations

Only in the early eighteenth century the worldwide expansion of our trade

1 Overture

Portsmouth in the late twentieth century looks very much like any of the large towns of southern England. Moving in from the surrounding country towards the centre, there is the same sequence of housing styles, going steadily backwards in time. Some of the meaner Victorian terraced housing seems as though it would be more at home several hundred miles further north in an industrial townscape; here perhaps is the first sign that this is not just another south-coast town. Beyond the business centre, there is a sudden change. There are cranes, the smell of salt water, and a high and seemingly continuous wall of old bricks, terminating the view down many of the streets. It is the wall round the Royal Naval Dockyard. Those long rows of houses which seem more appropriate to the industrial north were built to house many of the people who once worked there.

Only the Navy could safeguard England from invasion, and in the eighteenth century the worldwide expansion of our trade gave it the other increasingly important role of protecting shipping and commerce. Many of the great ships of England were built on the Thames, but in the eighteenth century Portsmouth grew to be one of the most important dockyards. The expansion of the Navy required the building of more new ships and increased the task of maintaining them. From the time of Pepys this required more and more men, with a greater burden of organisation. In the eighteenth century, as in the seventeenth, the Royal Dockyards were the largest concentrations of men and productive power in Britain. Nowhere else would several thousand be found at work in one establishment, and the quantities of materials also probably exceeded those needed in any other enterprise. The Frenchman, Blanqui, looking at the change which occurred in England after about 1770, likened it to the Revolution which had convulsed France, and called it 'the Industrial Revolution'. Until quite late in that revolution, the dockyards retained their position as the largest units of industry in Britain.

When, in 1793, Britain found herself at war with Revolutionary France under Napoleon's leadership, the increase in the size
of the Navy and of naval activity meant a corresponding
increase in the work of the dockyards, and in Portsmouth
especially the changes brought about by the Industrial Revolution had to be harnessed to the rising demands of war.
Mechanical power was only just beginning; most jobs still had
to be done by the power of men's arms, and large ships could
not be handled efficiently unless there was an abundant supply
of blocks and tackles. For replacement and new construction
the Navy needed 100,000 blocks every year, and these were
purchased mainly from the firm of Fox & Taylor of Southampton. Walter Taylor had greatly improved the block-making
process in the last quarter of the eighteenth century, but it was
left to Marc Brunel to bring the most advanced production
methods into Portsmouth dockyard in the form of block-making
machinery. While he was working in Portsmouth, a son, to be
christened Isambard, was born to him on 9 April 1806, in a
house in Britain Street, Portsea. The house was demolished in
the 1960s; the name of the little boy was to be immortal.

His mother, Sophie Kingdom, was the youngest child of
William Kingdom, a naval contractor of Plymouth, who had
died in the 1780s. Her mother sent Sophie to France at the end
of 1792 to learn French while staying at the house of M.
Carpentier in Rouen. Conditions in France were not so alarming, to Englishmen at any rate, as to make the decision a rash
one. Sophie, however, fell ill soon after arriving, and, as the
Terror in Paris mounted, the friends who had come with her
from England returned home. Shortly afterwards François
Carpentier got back to Rouen from a Paris which was aflame
with violence. He was accompanied by a young friend of the
family, called Marc Brunel. They had escaped only just in time,
for Brunel was a Royalist who had not concealed his views, and
the day after their departure barricades had been erected which
made it impossible to leave Paris freely.

Marc Brunel was the second son of an old-established family
of yeomen tenant farmers, from Hacqueville, near Gisors in
Normandy. The farm would go to his elder brother and family
tradition ordained that Marc should go into the Law or the
Church. His nature, however, was against both and at his first
school in Gisors he showed neither taste nor aptitude for the

classics, but excelled at mathematics and drawing. In 1780 his father, despairing of a son who spent his spare time drawing and hanging about the village wheelwright's shop, sent him to a seminary in Rouen. Both his talents and his shortcomings were recognized, and the Superior reversed his father's remedy for lack of progress, which had been chastisement and confinement. He encouraged Brunel's talents and recommended his father to choose some other calling for him, because he was clearly not for the Church.

The boy had often gone to the quays of Rouen where there were many unusual and interesting things to delight his enquiring mind. On one occasion he saw two cylinders for an early vertical steam engine, which had been unloaded from the ship bringing them from England. When he found out what they were, and whence they had come, he said: 'When I grow up I want to see that country.' In his father's eyes, however, the boy was a fool and a useless one at that; to the son's expressed desire to be an engineer he replied: 'You will only benefit the world, and starve yourself.' M. Brunel had a distant relationship in Rouen with M. Carpentier, who had retired from the sea, and this suggested a naval career for his son, so in 1782 young Marc left the seminary to live with the Carpentiers. He studied to become a naval cadet and his tutors were so accomplished in mathematics, drawing, and hydrography, that he must have found every day a joy, his eagerness to learn at last finding fulfilment in teaching which kept him at full stretch. The authorities were so happy with his progress that he was nominated as a cadet to a ship by no less a person than the king's Minister of Marine, and in 1786 he set sail for the West Indies.

Virtually nothing is known of Marc Brunel's activities while in the French navy, though the contemporary accounts of him as a youth suggest such a pleasant personality that it would be a surprise if he had not profited greatly from his time at sea, and been very popular. At the beginning of 1792 his ship came back to Rouen and paid off, Brunel returning to live with the Carpentiers. A year later the excursion to Paris with François Carpentier, which so nearly ended in disaster, took place. On their return to Rouen, a pleasant surprise awaited them in the shape of the charming, intelligent, and personable Miss Kingdom from England. For Marc, regard soon became affection, and, despite Mme, Carpentier's chaperonage, Marc Brunel and Sophie formed a deep attachment for one another. But Marc's days would end on the guillotine if he did not leave Rouen, for the hunt for Royalist sympathisers was on. Happily, a passport was obtained from the American vice-consul in Le Havre, and, on the pretext of going to America to buy grain for the forces, Brunel left France on 7 July 1793 on an American vessel appropriately named the *Liberty*, which arrived safely in New York early in September 1793. A new life was about to begin.

Brunel moved at once to Philadelphia, and shortly afterwards set off with two other passengers from the *Liberty* to survey what was to become part of New York State. They returned safely from what was then Indian country in the spring of 1794, and sailed down the Hudson from Albany to New York. During this journey the boat stuck for a day on a sandbank in the river, and an American merchant named Thurman came aboard. Brunel and his friends persuaded Thurman to finance the survey of a canal to join the River Hudson to Lake Champlain which drains into the River Richelieu leading northwards to the St. Lawrence. A successful survey was followed by the work of cutting the canal, and at this point Brunel seems to have decided not to go back to France, where the fall of Robespierre had ended the Terror, but to stay in America and become an engineer. His skill and energy soon gave him charge of the whole canal operation, and he was established in his new profession.

Sophie Kingdom, whom Brunel had left behind in Rouen, had not been so fortunate. She was not left unmolested for long after war broke out between England and France, and she was arrested in October 1793. Because ordinary prisons were filled to overflowing she was held in a convent at Gravelines near Calais. As the Terror grew more extreme, perhaps Sophie abandoned all hope. But when Robespierre fell in 1794, many of the lesser prisoners were released, and she found her way back to the Carpentiers in Rouen. In 1795 she managed to get back to England, and went to live in London with her elder brother. Somehow Brunel in New York re-established contact with her, telling her of his adventures. Although things were more peaceful in France, Brunel was doubtful if conditions there would be to his liking, and he certainly did not at that time intend to return, though always interested in news from across the Atlantic. Instead he seized other opportunities for advancing himself, and in 1796 he was appointed chief engineer of New York and became an American citizen.

One result of Brunel's naturalisation was a friendship with Alexander Hamilton, a protégé and close friend of George Washington. Hamilton was convinced that the actions of France might hold danger for his country, and the war in Europe was never far from his thoughts. At his house in 1798, Brunel met an *émigré* who had come from England. They discussed the value of the Royal Navy to England, and the difficulties of keeping it at sea. Prominent among these was the supply of blocks for the ships, and when the new guest described his visit to the Fox & Taylor block factory at Southampton, Brunel fancied he could improve on their methods, especially as so much seemed to be done by hand. Machinery designed for the purpose might permit much greater production. Hamilton encouraged his interest and, because of his pro-British sentiments, he was able to give Brunel a letter of introduction to Earl Spencer, First Lord of the Admiralty in Pitt's government. With his present commitments in New York finished, Brunel resigned as chief engineer and left for England at the end of January, 1799. At last he was to make good his boyhood promise to himself on the quay at Rouen.

After calling at Falmouth, the ship landed Brunel at Plymouth in March 1799, and he went straight to London, and to Sophie. She was now twenty-four and he almost thirty. The dashing young Royalist of Rouen, so romantic a figure, had become a man of affairs, and his charm and attraction for Sophie were undiminished. She too had matured, and had rejected a number of would-be suitors. The transatlantic correspondence had done its work; on 1 November 1799, they were married.

Brunel's task was now to make his way in London as he had in New York. Frenchmen of any kind were regarded with great suspicion at that time, but fortunately Brunel had Hamilton's introduction to the First Lord of the Admiralty. He also now had a brother-in-law who was an Under-secretary to the Navy Board.

There was, however, another great obstacle to be surmounted before Brunel could solve the Navy's problem of the supply of blocks: he had to convince those in authority of the benefits that his machines could bring. In 1800 very few people could understand drawings of machinery, and it would normally be quite beyond the experience of those in charge of the Admiralty.

Fortunately again, Brunel had brought with him knowledge of one of the greatest advances made in the art of producing engineering drawings. As a student he had been taught by Gaspard Monge, the man who invented the science of descriptive geometry, making it possible for a three-dimensional object to be accurately and completely described in a two-dimensional drawing, an essential tool as machines and engineering became the basis of great economic growth. Brunel had mastered this new art and, as it was a military secret in France till 1794, he was probably the first person to bring it to England.

But drawings, whether under the new system of Monge, or in the older, cruder manner, would not tell the men Brunel needed to convince what he wanted them to know. He needed working models. Solving this problem brought him into contact with a man whose contribution to mechanical engineering was at least as important as Monge's new science. Those Frenchmen who had escaped from the Revolution tended to draw together wherever they found themselves, and a fellow *émigré* named de Bacquancourt mentioned to Brunel that his complex models might be undertaken by a young craftsman then living at 64 Wells Street, just off Oxford Street, in London. His name was Henry Maudslay and he was the father of the machine tool. Maudslay's contribution was simple but fundamental: he designed machines which regulated their own work so that its exactness was a result of mechanical action, not of the operator's hand. The work turned out was precise beyond anything else then being made. Maudslay was probably the only man in England who could understand and produce what Brunel needed, and by 1801 he had made the models. Now the idea had to be sold to the blockmakers.

Although Fox & Taylor rejected Brunel's ideas, their contract was about to expire, and General Sir Samuel Bentham (brother of the philosopher, Jeremy Bentham), Inspector-general of Navy Works, was looking for ways of improving efficiency. He was convinced of the great benefits of mechanization and since his appointment in 1796 had been steadily improving the dockyards. Through Lord Spencer, Brunel met Bentham, and things moved rapidly. The models were demonstrated, the ideas accepted, and the Brunels moved to Portsmouth at the end of 1802 so that he could superintend the installation and working of the machinery in the dockyard. Marc was to be paid the equivalent of the savings to the Navy Board in one full year's production, so it was in his interest to wait for payment until the plant was expanded to its utmost size. Brunel hoped that the financial strain thus imposed would be justified, for he now had a growing family to support. Little Sophia had been born while they were still in London, and Emma was born in Portsmouth early in 1805; in April 1806 a son was born and he was christened Isambard after his father, and Kingdom after his mother.

This growing family naturally made its father give thought to the future. His successes with woodworking machinery at Portsmouth encouraged him to set up a sawmill and a veneer factory alongside the river at Battersea in partnership with a Mr. Farthing. Maudslay made the machinery, and the Brunels moved to Lindsey Row, Chelsea, in 1807. An examination of defective boots supplied to the Army led Brunel to produce in 1810 the machinery for making them. This too was installed at Battersea, and by 1812 large numbers of boots were being made. Things were going well in 1812, but there was trouble ahead.

First, the Battersea sawmill was burned down in 1814, and Brunel realized for the first time that Farthing's successor as his partner was a poor businessman, to say the least. Brunel's loss was severe. The end of the war with France in 1815, too, left him holding a large quantity of army boots which the government would not buy. Brunel might have been forgiven for losing faith in the government, with this example to add to their extreme dilatoriness over the money due to him for his work at Portsmouth.

Meanwhile his children were growing. Isambard had been learning drawing and geometry among other things from his father long before he went to a boarding-school run by Dr. Morell at Hove, and by 1820 was amusing himself making a plan of the town, which was then very small. We know little of his time at school except that he was full of high spirits, and seems to have found studying no more uncongenial than any other boy of fourteen. He had an active childhood untouched by serious illness. Lindsey Row faced the Thames, and from the steps in front of the house, Isambard learned to swim very well, an accomplishment which was to stand him in good stead years later. During one of his excursions into the flooded Thames tunnel, one of the party recorded that Brunel fell into the water.

'By the glimmering light from the entrance we found young Brunel, who swam like a fish, and soon got him on board.'

In November 1820, Isambard was sent to college at Caen in Normandy, and subsequently to the Lycée Henri Quatre in Paris, which was noted for its teaching of mathematics. At that time A. L. Breguet, one of the most famous watchmakers of his day, was working in Paris, and in 1821 young Brunel was apprenticed to him for a year.

But while young Isambard was in France, the storm which had been gathering on his father's horizon finally broke. His finances had never really recovered from the fire at the Battersea sawmills in 1814, and a succession of idle, incompetent, or dishonest business partners had not made matters any better. Marc Brunel's bankers failed in 1821, dragging him down with them. In May, Marc and his wife were committed to the King's Bench Prison at Southwark for debt. Sophie may have reflected that a debtors' prison was better than the convent of Gravelines, because at least there was no guillotine in the courtyard. But the enforced idleness weighed heavily on Marc Brunel. When, however, the outlook was bleak indeed, the Tsar of Russia sought his services (Brunel had met Alexander I when he had inspected the block-making machinery at Portsmouth) and the English government rapidly made the money available to pay his debts. 'The Misfortune', as it was ever after called in the family, had lasted just under three months, and Marc and Sophie were freed in August, 1821. Presumably such money as was needed to support Isambard in France had been discreetly forthcoming from kind friends; at all events, he did not return to England until August, 1822. He began immediately to help his father, who could have had no better assistant. Unlike many busy fathers, Marc had delighted in sharing with his children all that he was doing, never missing an opportunity to increase their knowledge and understanding. In addition, Isambard had done well in his formal education, and had profited greatly from the year spent with Breguet. Now his practical education was to begin. Isambard's next two years with his father were a broadening of experience, before he joined in the great adventure of the Thames tunnel.

2   The Thames Tunnel

When Isambard returned from France he was sixteen and his father fifty-three. This difference in ages might have produced a conflict which could have had only one ending: a determination to go their separate ways. Isambard was a high-spirited youth, and it would not have been surprising if he had thought his father cautious to an unacceptable degree. But, in fact, the relationship was quite different. Marc had been delighted that from boyhood Isambard had displayed the same enquiring mind, and many of the same interests and tastes as himself. How much more gratifying then, that, shortly after the start of his apprenticeship with Breguet, that most respected master should write of him in glowing terms: 'I think it is important to cultivate in him the happy inventive tendencies which he owes to nature or to education, and which it would be a great pity to see wasted.'

With 'The Misfortune' so fresh in her mind, his mother may well have wished for Isambard a career in some profession less hazardous to body and pocket than that which her husband was following. But to Isambard, this working with his father came as a natural delight, as well as a further broadening of knowledge. The relationship between father and son was exceptionally close, especially during the period up to the closure of the Thames tunnel works in 1828. Isambard's father had taught him drawing – 'the engineer's Alphabet' – and was always eager to share with him his knowledge and experience. In addition, although possessing the caution of experience, Marc was as bold an innovator as ever, and it is unlikely that Isambard ever felt his father holding back his ideas. From 1822 they shared the little office at No. 29, Poultry, in the City of London, along with a single clerk.

After the disasters of commerce, Marc Brunel's affairs were put into order, but, although he does not appear to have said so, it is clear that henceforth he would be acting as a designer and consultant engineer, rather than as a businessman. His aptitude for mechanical engineering often proved of great value, but from now on he concentrated more on works than machines. His experience at Portsmouth and Battersea enabled him to undertake several design tasks for the government, including ingenious sawmill plans for Chatham, Woolwich, and Trinidad. He also designed two suspension bridges for the French island of Réunion in the Indian Ocean.

There was also the Gaz engine, destined for years of patient, expensive, and eventually useless experiment. It depended upon the fact that gases can be liquefied by cooling. If the liquid gas was confined in a small space, an increase in temperature would cause an increase in pressure. By alternately raising and lowering the temperature, the pressure so generated could be used to drive machinery. Isambard was occupied on this device for much of his spare time in 1824 and 1825, but it never became more than an experiment. The pressures concerned were well over 1,000 lb. per square inch, and this caused nearly insuperable difficulties with materials. In addition there were the serious shortcomings of the production methods and technologies of the time, when locomotive engineers like Stephenson were having difficulty with keeping their machines steamtight at pressures of only 50 lb. per square inch. To be fair to the Brunels, Isambard's son in a 'Note on the Experiments with Carbonic Acid Gas' says that 'they were satisfied from an early period of the inquiry that the liquefied gases could only be advantageously employed where the cost of motive force was secondary to economy of space and to the avoidance of the cumbrous apparatus required for the use of steam.' Nobody has pursued the inquiry since, and it is a tribute to the Brunels' engineering skill that the engine and the experimenters were not blown up together.

The Brunels' next major project was closer to home: a tunnel under the Thames. Its origins can be traced to Marc's work on the problems of crossing the regularly icebound River Neva at St. Petersburg, about which the Tsar had consulted him in 1817. Marc had eventually produced a design for a bridge, having rejected the idea of tunnelling, chiefly perhaps because up till then nobody had ever successfully tunnelled under a river, although some had tried. In the early years of the nineteenth century London was growing rapidly down river from London Bridge, and much of this growth was connected with the new docks, which produced a lot of horse-drawn traffic. In 1802 a scheme for connecting Rotherhithe and Limehouse under the river had been started by a Cornish engineer, Robert Vazie, and although the great mine captain, mechanical engineer, and 'father of the locomotive' Trevithick had taken over the work, and actually dug a small-scale mining tunnel or drift from Rotherhithe to beyond the high-water mark on the other shore, the river kept breaking in through the roof, and the project was subsequently abandoned in 1807. Meanwhile, the rapidly-increasing traffic had to use the medieval London Bridge or go further up river.

The problem in digging under the river a tunnel large enough for wheeled traffic was that unless it was very deep it would have to pass through a mixed collection of clay, gravel, and sand, below the bed of the Thames. This meant that there would be the continual danger of the working-face falling in if the weight of the river above it burst through the intervening ground. In addition, not only the working-face but the roof and sides would have to be supported from within the tunnel until the permanent protection of brickwork could be built. In a small drift this could be done with timber, but not in a full-sized tunnel.

Nature provided the answer. At Chatham, Marc Brunel observed a beetle at work on some rotting timber and noticed that it used the shell-like front of its head to bore into even the hardest wood, which was then eaten and excreted, forming a hard lining to the 'tunnel' it dug. This gave Brunel the idea of an iron structure which he called a shield, which would support not only the working-face but also the roof and sides, preventing them from caving in while the permanent brickwork was being built behind it. Using hydraulic rams (an invention of Henry Maudslay's former employer, Joseph Bramah) the shield would be pushed forward as the tunnellers inside it 'ate' the ground. The idea was patented in 1818.

From Vazie's abortive attempt, it was known that beneath the Thames there were layers of gravel and sand, separated by layers of stiff, impervious clay. The gravel went down to about thirty-five feet, and somewhere below the seventy-foot mark was a deep and dangerous layer of quicksand. The tunnel would have to be dug in the band of about thirty-five foot thickness between these two strata, and it was thought that there was a three-foot layer of stiff clay at the top of this band, directly underlying the gravel, all the way across the river.

From the beginning of 1823, Brunel began to lobby men of influence for support for a tunnel company, and by 1824 a provisional committee was putting the scheme before the public. By July they had a Bill through Parliament and enough money in hand to start work. Mr Brunel was appointed engineer at £1,000 per annum. With Isambard at his side, and a small staff, detailed design work was already under way. Borings confirmed the strata which Vazie had found. The final designs of the shield were prepared and, to Brunel's relief, Maudslays got the job of making it. The Brunels moved from Chelsea to Bridge Street, Blackfriars, to be nearer the work, and on 2 March 1825, amid great junketings, Mr Smith, M.P., Chairman of the company, laid the first stone. The Great Bore had begun.

Before they could dig under the Thames, they needed a shaft about seventy feet deep. Vazie had been overwhelmed by water from the gravel through which his shaft had to pass to reach the dryer ground beneath the clay. Brunel needed a shaft fifty feet in diameter which the watery gravel would make almost impossible by ordinary methods. He therefore decided to build about half the depth of the shaft above the ground, and then excavate inside it so that, as the digging progressed, the structure gradually sank through the gravel under its own weight. They had some anxious moments, but the pumps managed to cope with the flow of water from the gravel because it was only exposed at the open bottom of the sinking shaft. When the pre-fabricated shaft had descended so that it was entirely in the ground, having passed right through the gravel and sealed it off, the lower part of the shaft was added by normal means. From this shaft, they could then drive the tunnel under the river, using Brunel's shield.

The tunnel was to be $37\frac{1}{2}$ feet wide and $22\frac{1}{4}$ feet high, with a rectangular section. This would completely encase the two oval archways, one for each roadway. The working-face for digging this rectangle was divided vertically into twelve sections, each three 'floors' high, making a total of thirty-six cells or 'boxes'. Each frame was supported on a huge iron foot, 'walking' on a transverse timber 'roadway'. On top of each frame, and at the outer side edges of numbers one and twelve, iron plates or 'staves' projected backwards to protect the top and sides of the hole the shield was making, until the brickwork encasing the archways was built up. The working-face of each 'box' was composed of fourteen horizontal 'poling boards', each held hard against the ground in front by two extending screw jacks. The other ends of these jacks or 'poling screws' bore against pockets in the side of the frame.

By this method each of the miners in the *odd*-numbered frames removing a poling board, shovelling out the earth to a depth of $4\frac{1}{2}$ inches behind it, and replacing it in an advanced position, having screwed out the poling-screw $4\frac{1}{2}$ inches to hold the board tightly against the earth. He then took out the next board below and repeated the process. The extended poling screws then bore against the pockets in the *even*-numbered frames, so that the odd-numbered frames were not receiving any backwards thrust from the ground. Each of these frames could then be advanced nine inches by screw-jacks bearing against the completed brickwork in the rear of them. The work of digging out another $4\frac{1}{2}$ inches of earth from behind each poling board in turn was then repeated, and, as each board was replaced a further $4\frac{1}{2}$ inches forward, its poling screw was screwed in $4\frac{1}{2}$ inches. Each board having now gone forward a total of nine inches, its poling screw could once more bear against the pockets in its own frame, as at the beginning. The end of this half-cycle left the odd-numbered frames standing nine inches ahead of the even-numbered ones, and in them another set of miners then proceeded to go through another half-cycle, so that at the end all twelve frames once more stood in line abreast across the tunnel. While their frames were not being worked forward, the miners adjusted the side and top staves, and carried out other tasks ready for their next half-cycle. Behind this activity came bricklayers, working in each of the two archways on wheeled timber staging, and laying bricks to form the permanent tunnel.

In November 1825 the tunnellers broke out from the base of the Rotherhithe shaft, which was now surmounted by a steam-engine which hoisted and lowered materials, pumped water out of the shaft, and drove a rope railway in the tunnel. Brunel was not employing contractors, and William Armstrong, the resident engineer, was in charge, under Marc Brunel's superintendence. Armstrong carried on until August 1826, but his health was deteriorating, and so was his grip on the work which became steadily more disorganized. In June, Marc's diary records: 'Isambard is the most efficient inspector we have. He is constantly in the work.'

When Armstrong gave up, Isambard became resident engineer in everything but name. He was given two assistants, Beamish and Gravatt, and they were sometimes in the tunnel for as long as twenty-four hours without a break. Although progress was being made under the river, there were increasing disputes among the directors as to how the work should be carried on, especially over the use of piecework rates which were causing poor and hurried work. As a result, a Committee of Works was appointed, and their authority and support enabled Marc Brunel to revert to a more ordered and secure method of working – only just in time, it seemed – because by the autumn of 1826 more and more water was seeping in round the shield. Isambard was indefatigable in restoring order and seeing that the work proceeded in a proper manner, and just before Christmas he was at last awarded the post of resident engineer at £200 a year.

Conditions underground got steadily worse, and there were 'runs' of water and mud, which occurred both in the 'boxes' and around and above the shield. Isambard's men became very skilled at dealing with the 'runs', and the use of a potent quick-setting 'Roman' cement mortar for the brickwork succeeded in keeping it intact and watertight. The worst problem was the very one which the shield had been designed to overcome. Between the shield and the brickwork there was always a gap which the bricklayers worked to fill, but this was a source of weakness. The water increased and with it came marsh gas, and there was much sickness among the miners. The three-foot band of stiff clay which should have been underneath the gravel and above their heads, keeping the river out, was not continuous. Despite Brunel's advice, the directors, beset by money worries, were admitting visitors – 'not all gentlemen', according to Isambard – although the danger was increasing with each high tide as the tunnel neared the half-way point. Isambard spent so much time in the tunnel that it became almost a second home. A New Year's dinner underground was followed in April by his coming-of-age party, which was celebrated with a concert in the western archway.

The most ominous sign of danger by now was that the water coming in at the face contained not just mud, but objects like brick and pottery from the bed of the river. On the night of 18 May 1827, disaster struck and the river broke into the tunnel.

Amidst the general panic, Isambard slid down with a rope into the flooded shaft to rescue one of the workmen, and fortunately nobody was killed. Next day, using a diving-bell suspended from a barge, Isambard and Gravatt went down into the river to see what had happened, and found that they had cut into a hole in the river-bed where it had been dredged for gravel. The hole thus formed had to be filled with bags of clay before the tunnelling could continue.

By 24 June the breach was filled, and the shaft pumped out so that Isambard and some companions could take a boat along the flooded tunnel. The Thames was a bitter enemy, and it was October before proper work could be restarted. At last the shield was intact again, and Isambard celebrated in the tunnel with a dinner for fifty, with music supplied by the band of the Coldstream Guards! In the adjoining archway, 100 workmen were also dining.

Progress, however, was very slow, as dissentient directors never failed to point out. Virtually everyone who worked in the tunnel was ill for varying periods. There is no doubt that, although the high wages to some extent compensated for the positively appalling conditions of work, the dangers pressed very heavily on the men. There was a lot of absenteeism, and the public houses in the area did a roaring trade when the shifts changed, especially if the men had just been paid. Sundays were not normally working days, but sometimes the almost liquid state of the ground made it dangerous to stop work. Then the digging went on without a break, always in the hope of reaching somewhat firmer ground.

Lighting and ventilation were other problems. At first, portable cylinders of liquid gas, each with a burner on top, were used, and, although these sound rather like primitive fire-bombs, no serious accidents occurred. A piped gas-lighting supply was refused by the directors in June 1826, but the revenue from visitors and the very real need for better light persuaded them to change their minds, and it was installed by March of the following year. The design of the tunnel as two archways within a rectangle of solid brickwork had provided a small ventilating tunnel in the upper part of the brickwork, and the furnace of the steam-engine above the Rotherhithe shaft drew its air through it. The first irruption of the river blocked this ventilating tunnel and wrecked the lighting system, so that the work of clearing away the debris and mud had to go on by the light of candles and portable gas-cylinders. The blocked ventilator was never cleared, and it was some time before a temporary wooden one, never very effective, was provided.

Some of the directors, and especially Smith, the Chairman, constantly badgered Brunel with schemes, put up by their friends, for doing the work more quickly. Luckily the company's engineer was well supported by other directors, and perhaps they all knew at heart that he was the only man who could complete the tunnel. He was left in charge, assisted by his son, Beamish, and Gravatt. Often they could work only on the ebb tide, when there was less chance of the river breaking in. Early in the morning of 12 January 1828, however, there was a massive irruption which flooded the tunnel again. There had been signs that ground conditions were improving, and Isambard had been at the shield all night. When the morning shift came on at 6 a.m., he put two of his best miners, Ball and Collins, to work at the most difficult and dangerous spot, the top left-hand corner of the shield. His report to the directors tells what happened.

We began to work the ground at the west top corner of the frame: the tide had just begun to flow, and finding the ground tolerably quiet, we proceeded by beginning at the top, and had worked about a foot downwards, when, on exposing the next six inches, the ground swelled suddenly and a large quantity burst through the opening thus made. This was followed instantly by a large body of water. The rush was so violent as to force the man on the spot, where the burst took place, out of the cell ('box') on to the timber stage behind the frames. I was in the frame with the man, but upon the rush of water I went into the next cell in order to command a better view of the irruption, and seeing there was no possibility of then opposing the water, I ordered all the men in the frames to retire – all men retiring except the three men who were with me, and they retreated with me. I did not leave the stage until those three men were down the ladder of the frame, when they and I proceeded about twenty feet along the west arch of the Tunnel. At this moment the agitation of the air, by the rush of water, was such as to extinguish all the lights, and the water had gained the height of the middle of our waists. I was at that moment giving directions to the three men in what manner they ought to proceed in the dark to effect their escape, when they and I were knocked down and covered by a part of the timber stage. I struggled under water for some time and at length extricated myself from the stage; and by swimming and being forced by the water, I gained the eastern arch when I got a better footing, and was enabled by laying hold of a rope, to pause a little, in the hope of encouraging the men who had been knocked down with myself.

This I endeavoured to do by calling to them. Before I reached the shaft the water had risen so rapidly that I was out of my depth, and therefore swam to the Visitors' Stairs, the stairs of the workmen being occupied by those who had so far escaped. My knee was so injured by the timber stage that I could scarcely swim or get up the stairs, but the rush of water carried me up the shaft. The three men who had been knocked down with me were unable to extricate themselves, and I grieve to say they were lost; also two old men and one young man in other parts of the work.

His assistant, Beamish, who was in the office on the surface, was called to the top of the shaft by the watchman and, being unable to get down the workmen's stairs because of those coming up, broke down the door to the visitors' stairs, and started to go down them. A great wave of water carried Isambard Brunel up to the surface, and Beamish rescued him. ' "Ball! Ball! – Collins! Collins!" were the only words he could for some time utter; but the well-known voices answered not – they were forever silent,' wrote Beamish in his account of what happened.

Isambard lived to fight again another day, though never, as it turned out, in the making of the tunnel. Although he tried to supervise diving-bell operations on the day after the water broke in, he was too ill and had to be put to bed. His journal records his feelings.

I have now been laid up quite useless for 14 weeks and upwards, ever since 14th January. I shan't forget that day in a hurry, very near finished my journey then; when the danger is over, it is rather amusing than otherwise – while it existed I can't say the feeling was at all uncomfortable. If I was to say the contrary, I should be nearer the truth in this instance. While exertions could still be made and hope remained of stopping the ground it was an excitement that has always been a luxury to me. When we were obliged to run, I felt nothing in particular; I was only thinking of the best way of getting us on, and the probable state of the arches.

When knocked down, I certainly gave myself up, but I took it very much as a matter of course, which I had expected the moment we quitted the frames, for I never expected we should get out. The instant I disengaged myself and got breath again – all dark – I bolted into the other arch – this saved me by laying hold of the railrope. I stood still nearly a minute. I was anxious for poor Ball and Collins, who I felt too sure had never risen from the fall we had all had and were, as I thought, crushed under the great stage. I kept calling them by name to encourage them and make them also (if still able) come through the opening. I was then obliged to be off – but up to that moment, as far as my sensations were concerned, and distinct from the idea of the loss of six poor fellows whose death I could not then foresee, kept there.

The sight and the whole affair was well worth the risk and I would willingly pay my share, £50 about, of the expense of such a 'spectacle'. Reaching the shaft I was much too bothered with my knee and some other thumps to remember much.

If I had been kept under another minute when knocked down I should not have suffered more, and I trust I was tolerably fit to die. If, therefore, the occurrence itself was rather a gratification than otherwise and the consequences in no way unpleasant, I need not attempt to avoid such.

Although the obvious injury was to his knee, in fact he was also injured internally. Convalescence was followed by a trip to Brighton for a rest, but the delights of that convivial town were too much for him and he had a relapse with repeated haemorrhages which kept him in bed till August.

The second flooding broke the finances of the company. Although they were supported by the Duke of Wellington and many other great men, the public would not invest any more money. The breach in the river-bed was sealed, and the tunnel cleared, but they had to stop. In August, the twin bores of the tunnel were bricked up, with the frames still in place, and Marc Brunel resigned.

The remainder of the tunnel's story can be briefly told. In 1829 a loan from the government was the company's sole hope, but that was possible only if the directors could resolve their differences, and offer some real hope that they would in fact be able to finish the job. After a great deal of wrangling, the anti-Brunel party, headed by Smith, was defeated in 1832, and work restarted in 1835. Three times more the river broke in, but in 1839 they finally reached the Wapping shore, and on 16 November 1841 the tunnel was finished. Marc Brunel, now seventy-two, had been knighted in March, but almost immediately his health broke down. He recovered, however, to enjoy at last his rightful triumph when the tunnel was opened to the public on 25 March 1843. Since 1869 the tunnel has carried a railway, now the London Transport line serving East London.

3 Bridge-builder

Isambard's period of convalescence after the water broke in a second time was prolonged, and he had ample time for reflection. He imagined that the tunnel was abandoned forever, that this would drive his father to the grave, and that his father's death would be quickly followed by that of his mother, leaving him alone.

I suppose a sort of middle path will be the most likely one [for me] – a mediocre success – an engineer sometimes employed, sometimes not – £200 or £300 a year and that uncertain: well, I shall then have plenty to wish for and that always constituted my happiness. May I always be of the same mind and then the less I have the happier I shall be.

I'll turn misanthrope, get a huge Meerschaum, as big as myself, and smoke away melancholy – and yet that can't be done without money and that can't be got without working for it. Dear me, what a world this is where starvation itself is an expensive luxury. But damn all croaking, the Tunnel must go on, it shall go on. By the by, why should I not get some situation, surely I have friends enough for that. Q. – Get a snug little berth and a snug little wife with a little something to assist in housekeeping? What an interesting situation! No luxuries, none of your enjoyments of which I am tolerably fond? – Oh! – horrible.

Coming back from his holiday in France at the beginning of 1829, Isambard fell in with two companions of his own age, and one of them, Charles MacFarlane, in his *Reminiscences of a Literary Life,* has left us a portrait of Isambard then. 'A little, nimble, dark-complexioned man, who did not look more than five- or six-and-twenty. He had a vast deal of ready, poignant wit, and some of his repartees were admirable.' Isambard had inherited from his father an optimistic and energetic temperament, and he believed in the older man's motto in adversity: 'Courage! A man who can do something and keep a warm, sanguine heart will never starve.' Having read of his feelings as he stood in one half of the tunnel positively admiring the grand spectacle of the flooding of the other half – which he knew would soon engulf him – we cannot doubt his courage.

That courage was one of the things that enabled him to get the best out of his men, for he spent a lot of his time in the tunnel, much of it in the shield, sharing hardship and danger with them. He believed that they would respond more readily to his presence on the spot than to orders from a comfortable office on the surface at Cow Court. Furthermore he was just, and had no favourites, and whenever the occasion arose, he had the happy knack of doing the thing which would more firmly identify him with his men, though always as their chief. When the water won a temporary victory, he always led the way back after it had been driven out, and always accompanied by those whom he called his *corps d'élite*, who had been the last to leave their posts when the water came in. Then there were things, too, like the dinner in the tunnel. The men loved a show, and they loved him, because he arranged for them to share in it, though not in a way that would cause them embarrassment, as for instance by mixing them at table with their superiors. These touches – his knowledge and courage and his flair for doing the right thing – made Brunel their real leader. At the dinner-table he received from the chairman of the workmen's dinner the symbols of the miner's craft, a pickaxe and a spade.

The Brunels had been reduced to a very modest existence at the time the tunnel was started in 1825, and it was natural that Isambard should reflect then on how he was going to make his fortune.

Perhaps the Gaz Engine, if it is good for anything, will only be tolerably good, and perhaps make us spend a good deal of money; that I should pass through life as most other people do, and that I should gradually forget my castles in the air, live in a small house, and at most keep my gig. On the other side it may be much worse. My father may die, or the Tunnel may fail and I most likely in such circumstances, cut my throat or hang myself. But, whatever may turn out, I should, in imagination, have enjoyed my fortune for at least a year or two, without doing anybody harm.

But gloom did not prevail. His great friend was William Hawes, brother of Benjamin Hawes who had married his sister, Sophia, and during the years of the tunnel they went together on excursions to town and country. Nor were his friends exclusively male. A few months after the sombre thoughts of cutting his own throat, his journal records:

Went down in the steamboat with M.C. I do not know what to think of myself. I have made love openly to C.H. and received a return and doing the same thing with M.C. here. She has made a fool of me, and I of her.

A surplus of young ladies was, however, less of a problem to Isambard than the immediate future. Ambitious and energetic, and confident of his own knowledge and ability, his task now was to turn these talents into employment and income; but he need not have worried. When Isambard was well enough to be allowed up, he went for convalescence, not to Brighton again, but to Clifton, a healthy suburb of Bristol, and it was in Bristol that he really began an independent career for himself.

The gorge of the River Avon cuts through the Downs on the north-western side of Bristol, dividing Clifton from Leigh Down, and for many years it had been intended to bridge the gorge at this point. In 1829, shortly after Isambard had returned from France, matters came to a head and a design competition was opened. A friend in Bristol passed the news to Isambard, and the Clifton bridge project turned out to be Isambard's path to fame and fortune.

The story of the bridge at Clifton began in 1753, when Alderman William Vick bequeathed £1,000 to the Society of Merchant Venturers in Bristol, to accumulate interest until it reached £10,000 for which, the alderman had been told, a stone bridge could be built across the gorge. By 1829 £8,000 was available and a committee was appointed to give substance to Vick's dream, but it was soon realized that this sum would not now be nearly enough for the purpose, and that the public would have to take shares in a bridge company.

An open competition produced twenty-two plans, and those of Isambard Brunel and four others were placed on a short list. The gorge at Clifton is seven hundred feet wide and over two hundred feet deep, and Brunel's plan was to span straight across without the great expense of any intermediate supporting piers; his experience in helping his father with the designs for bridges in Réunion led him to propose a suspension bridge. In fact, he put in four alternative designs. The one he himself favoured could be built without the need for the usual towers to carry the suspension chains. The chains would be anchored in the top of the cliffs on either side; the roadway would be approached by cuttings or tunnels leading down from the upper level of the Downs.

The foremost bridge-designer in Britain at that time was Thomas Telford, and the committee asked him to judge the various plans. Even the shortest of Brunel's bridges was longer than Telford's own masterpiece, the six-hundred-foot bridge over the Menai Straits, and Telford was of the opinion that winds blowing through the Avon gorge would bring down a suspension bridge of the length which Brunel proposed. In the work on the Réunion bridges, winds of hurricane force had caused Marc Brunel to adopt an ingenious method of bracing the bridge at each side by an extra pair of chains, and Isambard's longest Clifton design incorporated the idea, but this does not seem to have satisfied Telford. His views on maximum span, which caused Isambard to withdraw his designs, were based on the behaviour of his Menai bridge in high winds, when alarming movement had occurred, resulting in considerable damage. As Telford could not bring himself to recommend any of the other competitors, he was asked to prepare a design himself. He proposed a suspension bridge with huge intermediate piers on either bank of the river, the whole edifice to be executed in the Gothic style then becoming so fashionable. While the site needed piers that suggested brooding strength to harmonize with the rugged surroundings, Telford's design in the Gothic style achieved great strength without the appearance of massive proportions, and would have appeared somewhat out of place across the Avon gorge.

Telford's plan was also rejected, reluctantly 'on account of the inadequacy of the funds requisite for meeting the cost of such high and massive towers as were essential to the plan which that distinguished individual had proposed.' This at any rate was the reason given for not even including it in a second short list after the competition had been reopened; perhaps the good people of Bristol knew a bad thing when they saw it. After some arguments about detail, Isambard's design for a shorter suspension bridge of seven hundred feet was adopted, with a great abutment on the Somerset side of the river. The towers to carry the suspension chains were of a squat, massive character, tapering inwards from bottom to top, and capped with projecting stone monoliths. This tapering style was Egyptian, and it obviously went down very well with the committee, not only because it was fashionable but also because it was much cheaper to build.

'The Egyptian thing I brought down was quite extravagantly admired by all and unanimously adopted,' wrote Isambard, who evidently considered his achievement of producing agreement about style among the fifteen committee members almost as great as that of gaining their award. His skill as an artist is shown by the fact that the bridge roadway rises towards the Gloucestershire side of the gorge, because the land there is slightly higher than on the Somerset side, and a dead level bridge would have appeared to be going downhill. It is a small detail, but one which points to the artist in the engineer.

A purely ceremonial start was made on the Clifton side three months later, but although Alderman Vick's legacy had been augmented by public subscriptions, in 1831 there was not enough money for serious work to start. Nevertheless, by winning the competition, Isambard Brunel had become a person of note in Bristol. Unfortunately, England was moving towards a period of great social and political disturbance, which made the raising of funds extremely difficult.

The years of economic depression which followed Waterloo had given place, with interruptions, to a great acceleration of growth of the British economy, as the Factory Revolution spread to the making of more and more products. The effect was cumulative, and it brought increasing economic power to a new class of men, the so-called 'middle orders' in society, distinguished from today's middle classes by their possession of considerable personal wealth, as well as relatively high income. Although many of them followed the traditional English course of buying land with some of their wealth, land ownership was often nothing more than an enjoyment of this wealth in a traditional way. The source of their wealth was commerce and industry, and the professions as in the case of the Brunels. Because their wealth did not come from the land, they rarely acquired the local political power which came through land ownership over many generations.

In 1830 Parliament was much as it had been at the end of the seventeenth century, representing mainly 'the landed interest' and not the common people or the rising men of industry and commerce. The time for a change had come, but in 1831 the House of Commons narrowly rejected the Reform Bill, and a general election was held. After the election the Bill was passed by the Commons, but thrown out by the House of Lords, and a constitutional crisis of the first magnitude followed.

In the country the ordinary people believed that the reform of Parliament would bring them substantial benefits, and their support of the movement for reform put the well-to-do in something of a quandary. On the one hand they wanted reform; on the other, they were afraid that reform might be followed by revolution. In such disturbed times, it is not surprising that people with money were reluctant to invest it in projects of any kind, particularly such imaginative schemes as the Clifton bridge.

With the Lords and Commons locked in combat, public opinion in Bristol boiled over on 29 October 1831, and for three days serious rioting took place, sparked off by the arrival for the Quarter Sessions of the Recorder, Sir Charles Wetherall, accounted one of the most intransigent opponents of Reform. The civic authorities were very reluctant to make firm use of the troops at their disposal, and perhaps the troops themselves had some sympathy with the rioters. Their commander, Col. Brereton, seems to have lacked either resolution or firm directives from the magistrates. When ordered to do so, the soldiers dispersed the mob, but at least theirs was not the lot of the regular troops called in to deal with the 'Peterloo' riots in Manchester in 1819. On that infamous occasion, the yeomanry who were mainly drawn from the class of small shopkeepers and the like, were the main assailants of the fleeing rioters, and the 'redcoats' had to intervene repeatedly to prevent unnecessary violence. In Bristol, Col. Brereton sent the yeomanry away, perhaps being anxious not to inflame the mob, but carrying this reluctance too far. He shot himself during his subsequent court martial.

Lest the affair be thought a massacre, the Annual Register records that four people died at the hands of the military, as against two from excessive drinking and five who were burned alive in the buildings they themselves had set on fire. The Bristol riots were not really political, but an excuse for looting and plunder, and against this Brunel, who was staying at Clifton, joined with other respectable men, Whig and Tory.

With Bristol so disturbed and money so tight, there was little prospect of the Clifton bridge going ahead, and after the riots Isambard returned to London where he learned of a proposal to build docks on either side of the River Wear at Sunderland. He immediately went north and made himself known to one of the committees who were putting forward a scheme for an enclosed dock. Up to that time, the sailing vessels which carried the coal from the Wear area of the Durham coalfields were grounded on the mud at low tide, and this restricted the amount of coal that could be shipped. Two groups of merchants in Sunderland were contending for the right to construct enclosed docks so that loading could go on continuously.

Isambard designed a scheme for the northern group, whose dock was to be at Monkwearmouth, opposite Sunderland. Both factions applied to Parliament for the necessary powers. After such a Bill had been formally read a first time, it was debated and voted on, and passed to a committee of Members for detailed examination. This took the form of a semi-judicial hearing, to bring out in detail all the important points. Bullying of the weaker witnesses by hostile Counsel was common, and any witness who was unknown but important to the case might be subjected to a dose of it, which generally stopped if he gave as good as he got. When Isambard made his first appearance before the parliamentary committees, he was only twenty-five, and without any works of note to his credit. Some attempt was made to unsettle him by referring to his inexperience in comparison with Francis Giles, the engineer for the rival southern docks, and an old adversary from the days of the Thames tunnel, when he was associated with the directors hostile to the Brunels. However, he refused to be rattled, and was able to give a good account of himself. In the event, neither scheme came to anything at that time.

Happily the Monkwearmouth scheme came alive again after this setback, and in 1834 the Wearmouth Dock Company was incorporated by royal charter. The moving spirits behind it were Sir Hedworth Williamson and his family, who as owners of much of the land on the north side of the Wear opposite Sunderland, had been interested in the earlier proposal. The seventh Baronet and his brother raised £60,000 and Brunel designed the dock, on a smaller scale than that of 1831. It was completed in 1836 but the cost was £120,000, a figure which greatly displeased its promoters. The dock was not a commercial success, and in 1845 sold to George Hudson, the 'Railway King', for £85,000, passing through his Newcastle and Darlington

Junction Railway Company to the North Eastern Railway Company, and thence eventually into public ownership. Virtually all trace of it has been obliterated in recent years.

The Monkwearmouth docks, nevertheless, marked a turning point in Isambard's career. In 1832, Monkwearmouth seemed destined to join Clifton bridge and a double-deck railway bridge across the Wear in a series of abortive schemes, and he seemed to be making very little progress as an engineer, though he was in fact earning a living. The only real success for the family was when Benjamin Hawes, who had married Sophia, was elected to the first reformed Parliament as a Radical for the newly-formed constituency of Lambeth. Both Marc and Isambard helped in the election. But the election was important in another way; it led to a revival of business confidence and prosperity, in which Isambard shared in full measure.

Unlike Monkwearmouth, Bristol was not closely connected with the coal industry, and her trade was steadily declining. Bristol's port was where the small River Frome joins the larger Avon, about six miles from the sea, and, after a steady growth of trade over many centuries, a number of commercial factors began to effect it adversely. Bristolians attributed the decline in their trade in part to poor shipping facilities, and to improve them and prevent further loss of trade, they proposed to change part of the Avon in the city into an enclosed harbour, and to make a new course for the river, the 'New Cut'. This was done by 1809, but at about the same time the dues payable by ships using the new enclosed harbour, or 'Float' as it was called, were increased. But Bristol's troubles were more serious. In the north, Liverpool and Glasgow were thriving on the great expansion of cotton production in the factories, at the expense of older-established trade in woollen cloth from Gloucestershire and Somerset; and the ending of the slave trade – so closely connected with Bristol's major trades of tobacco and sugar – made matters worse. Bristol began to be left behind, and the decline was hastened by the formation of shoals in the Float.

At its upper end there was a dam which allowed the New Cut to be fed with water only when the Avon was flowing above a certain height. If the river was below this level, the water passed into the Float, and out through the half-tidal Cumberland Basin at the lower end, where there were locks into the river. The Float was divided about half way along by the

Prince's Street drawbridge, near which was an intermediate entrance from the New Cut. The shoals in the Float were caused by silt brought down both by the Avon and the smaller Frome, which also fed into the enclosed harbour, and ships often ran aground, having to be hauled up to the quays with ropes and winches, causing both expense and delay. The original design of the Float had provided that from time to time all the water could be caused to flow through only one half of the channel, so scouring the mud away, but as this meant losing the use of half the harbour for a period this necessary but unpopular practice fell into disuse. Hence the shoals.

The impediments to shipping and the loss of trade and revenue had reached such proportions that the dock company resolved to put matters right, before it was too late. Isambard's work on the Clifton bridge project had brought him into contact with many of the leading men of business in Bristol, for the Merchant Venturers Society had been entrusted with Alderman Vick's legacy. It was one of these friends, Nicolas Roch, who introduced the subject of the floating harbour to Brunel, and his ensuing report was acted upon by the dock company.

Isambard had to face two associated problems. The first was to reduce the deposit of silt in the Float, and the second was to improve the means of getting rid of the silt which accumulated despite the improvements. The Neetham Dam controlled the flow of water into the New Cut, but it was in such a bad state that even when the Avon was low, some of its water passed into the New Cut rather than through the Float to help keep it clear. If this dam were put in order and raised, the flow of water through the Float would be increased, so that shoals of silt would be less likely to form. This would reduce the problem to the point where it could be dealt with by two or three thorough scourings each year.

In order to deal with the existing shoals, and to make the scourings more effective, Brunel designed a boat which could scrape the walls and bottom of the Float and the Cumberland Basin. The silt would be dragged to the lower end of the Float where it joined the Cumberland Basin by what were called the Junction Locks. At that point only about 250 yards separated the Float from the New Cut and Brunel proposed a special culvert into the latter, so that the silt could be scoured into the New Cut at low tide.

The solutions to the two problems were interdependent, and both needed money, which in Bristol, so recently torn by riots, was not easy to find. As a result, when the work was put in hand at the beginning of 1833, only a part of Brunel's scheme of improvements was carried out. The essential improvement to the supply of water into the Float, which would have prevented the formation of new shoals, was neglected. After a period of improvement, therefore, silt began to build up again. Nevertheless, some of the work was done, and Isambard had been given the job of doing it, and thus the association of his name with two major public works in Bristol advanced his reputation.

Just as the plans for the Clifton Bridge had brought Brunel into contact with Roch, and hence the dock company, so his work brought him two other important acquaintances. Mr. Osborne was a solicitor who at first did not seem favourably disposed towards Brunel: ' . . . Osborne, the Solicitor, is trying to prejudice me in the manner which has so much power, viz. by throwing out hints and illusions [*sic*] to my motives, and catching at every movement to make his remarks.'[1] Things obviously improved, because the dock company work brought them together and gave the solicitor a closer view of Isambard's abilities, which he was perceptive enough to note from a fairly early stage. The second friend was Captain Christopher Claxton, a naval officer on half-pay. Exactly how they first met we do not know; perhaps it was owing to Claxton's position as Quay Warden of Bristol. It would be fascinating to speculate if Isambard in 1831 was one of 'two or three gentlemen who hastened to defend Capt. Claxton's residence when the mob threatened it, and drove them off so saving his property.'[2] At any rate they remained firm friends for life.

Although matters in Bristol were so depressed, and work on both the Clifton bridge and the docks in abeyance, things were nevertheless moving. Men of vision had realized that what the Liverpool and Manchester Railway of 1830 had done for Liverpool, a railway to London might do for Bristol, especially if the docks were improved. A private meeting in the autumn of 1833 set things going. Business conditions were improving

1. Once he had realised Brunel's integrity and abilities, Osborne became a staunch friend.

2. The Bristol riots were the excuse for a great deal of looting by many of those *other* than the rioters and drunken mobs.

in 1833, and Roch of the dock company was one of the group of men who were considering the appointment of an engineer for the preliminary survey of a line of railway. By this time the works on the Float were in hand, and on 21 February 1833, in Osborne's office, Roch told Brunel about the committee on the railway project. Would Brunel allow his name to go forward? He did, and one senses an element of gamble on his part. With so many rather lukewarm irons in the fire, why not add another? Similar applications in 1830 to the Newcastle and Carlisle Railway and to the Birmingham and Bristol Railway, though supported by influential patrons, had come to nothing, but something might come of this one.

4   Birth of the Great Western Railway

The meeting with the promoters of the Bristol and London Railway was the beginning of the enterprise by which Brunel became one of the leaders of the civil engineering profession, and it is a proper moment for us to take stock of the man. Isambard at twenty-six had crowded more incident and high adventure into his years than many men do into a lifetime. All those who came into contact with him were impressed by the depth and thoroughness of his thought, the breadth of his interests, and the vivacity of his sense of enquiry. Brunel seems to have had no doubt of his own ability, though he was modest enough to confine his thoughts to the pages of his diary.

Practically, and then in name, he had occupied the most exacting post of resident engineer of the Thames tunnel for seventeen months, and there he had gained invaluable experience. It was a very arduous job, demanding not only the arts and skills of the engineering profession, but also negotiating ability, diplomacy, tenacity, and energy. The tunnel also called for courage of a high order, and this too, was there. It would be difficult to think of a more testing and yet rewarding start to his career; the mutual inspiration and support between father and son must often have been the only thing that enabled them to keep on.

The Thames tunnel had brought the name of Brunel to the forefront in Britain, but it was a name not yet crowned with success, as the works lay deserted, partly flooded, bricked up, and, for all anyone knew of the future, abandoned. Isambard had then struck out on his own, becoming involved in the various dock schemes and, most notably, in the Clifton bridge project. In these he had gained the experience which the tunnel had not provided: taking on his own shoulders, unaided, the design and construction of major works. He could rely on assistance and advice from his father at any time, but his father was in London, and at Monkwearmouth and Bristol Isambard really stood alone.

Of these two places, Bristol proved the more rewarding, and started a connexion which was to stand him in good stead. His Clifton bridge designs had made his name well known in Bristol, and his work in the docks enlarged his reputation locally. At this period he might have been called a rising 'Bristol man', and to some extent he remained a Bristol man all his life. In 1839 he wrote 'as a Bristol man which from 10 years connexion I may say I have become', and right at the end of his life, although, as always, dreadfully busy, he wrote to the Bristol Dock Company offering his services, for old times' sake, in connexion with some improvement scheme.

These activities had also brought him into contact with men of great influence locally; men like Roch and Osborne. These men of business, rather than the great landowners, were the force and energy behind the attempt to revive Bristol's dying trade, and Brunel was a rising man among them.

The year 1833 was a year of returning confidence in Britain. This stemmed, at least in part, from the election of the reformed Parliament where for the first time that class of people of 'the middling sort' were represented and active, and among them, Brunel had many friends. The potential for economic growth was so great that, when businessmen overcame their timidity, in 1836 there was a commercial crisis due to speculation. An essential part of this potential was the coming of the railways. The achievements of the Stockton and Darlington Railway Company after 1825 demonstrated the superiority of railways over canals, and the practicability of the steam locomotive. The successful Liverpool and Manchester Railway had a much wider impact. As Dionysius Lardner said in 1835, 'the opinions of scientific men have wholly changed since the formation of the Liverpool and Manchester Railway – it came upon the scientific world like a miracle.' The effect on the world of business was no less. It demonstrated both the very real utility of steam railways to the trade and industry which they served, and the profits to be made in the process. It also gave birth to the great trunk line schemes by which, at the end of the decade, railways to link every major commercial and industrial centre would be projected or building.

The first of these schemes proposed to link Liverpool, Manchester, and the still rapidly growing industrial area of south Lancashire, with Birmingham, and then with London. The projects were called respectively the Grand Junction Railway, and London and Birmingham Railway, and they came before Parliament in 1833, attracting a great deal of attention and interest. All the other railways in existence (or coming into being) were essentially local lines (like the Canterbury and Whitstable line of 1829) or lines with a strongly industrial bias, usually connected with coal or iron; but these new trunk lines commanded the stage because of their size and the changes they would bring about over such a wide area. With the trunk lines came the engineers whose names were to become widely known in railway and business circles in the next few years.

Civil engineering was an offshoot of fortification or military engineering, which had grown greatly in sophistication in the seventeenth century. In the eighteenth century civil engineering was mainly concerned with the building of bridges and docks, and improving rivers, but the growth of canals after Brindley's success in 1761 had advanced techniques and increased the numbers of people in the profession, because canals needed works on a larger scale than anything previously done in England. The rising generation of engineers was busy – as the Brunels were – with docks and canals, and the new railways offered still greater and more challenging tasks.

In 1833 George Stephenson towered in public estimation far above those who were known as railway engineers. He remained a plain man all his life, yet we can detect real respect in the attitude adopted towards him by the lawyers practising before the parliamentary committees. He was listened to with care, and his words carried great weight. Although withdrawing from full participation in railway affairs as he grew old, he retained this respect, both for his work as a pioneer and for his integrity. Brunel, like the other rising men, acknowledged his seniority – 'our respected Grandfather, George Stephenson' he called him in a letter to George Hudson in 1844. Stephenson's son, Robert, however, was more nearly Brunel's contemporary. Railway engineering was emerging from the age of empirical endeavour, where George Stephenson's experience, intuition, and tenacity had won him such a great reputation, and, as Isambard Brunel entered upon his railway career, it was becoming more an exact science. In 1833 Robert Stephenson was emerging from the shadow of his father's reputation, being pushed, embarassingly at times, by George, who wanted success and fame for his son. By contrast, Isambard Brunel in 1833 was the son of Mr. Brunel, the engineer of the Thames tunnel, having an independent reputation only in Bristol.

Brunel was not the only man to be considered by the Bristol promoters of a railway to London. William Brunton and H. H. Price had already surveyed a line to London in the previous year. There was also W. H. Townsend, a surveyor who was superintending the building of the Bristol and Gloucestershire Railway, a purely local line known as the 'Coalpit Heath Tramway'. The committee, seeking to decide between the rival contenders, proposed to ask each to make a survey, choosing the engineer whose scheme was the cheapest. Brunel thought this a bad idea, and said so, although his friend, Roch, favoured the competition plan. Brunel gave his objection in a letter to the committee:

'You are holding out a premium', he wrote, 'to the man who will make you the most flattering promises, and it is quite obvious that the man who has the least reputation at stake, or the most to gain by temporary success, and the least to lose by the consequences of a disappointment, must be the winner in such a race.'

If they persisted in their competition, he would withdraw; the proceedings connected with his Clifton bridge design had perhaps given him his fill of competitions. Not all the committee favoured a competition of this nature, and Brunel's letter persuaded the promoters to abandon the idea. He did not attempt to lobby the committee members; instead he went to London for the annual meeting of the tunnel company, returning to Bristol through the night of 6 March. In the morning the decision went his way, though by a majority of only one, and he was thereupon formally appointed.

Townsend was to assist him in the outline survey, which was to be completed by May. When the Bill was before the House of Lords Committee in 1835, Brunel was questioned as to the instructions which had been given him regarding this first survey. He was quite clear what those instructions were. They directed, generally, his attention 'not only to find the best line between Bristol and London, but also to have regard to Gloucester and South Wales.' A revealing phrase which is also used is 'between the Metropolis and the West of England', which suggests that, from the very beginning, both the promoters and

their engineer were aware that there was more to their undertaking than just joining London and Bristol, although how
wide their vision actually was remains a matter of speculation.

Brunel and Townsend were a very unequal partnership, a
fact which both recognized; but neither underestimated the
difficulty of their task. The selection of a route was quite impossible without deciding upon the levels of the line, and this
required a knowledge of the altitude at many different points
across country. The Ordnance Survey had been started in 1791
but, although the surveyors were able to use this for planning,
the best map available in 1833 was not accurate enough for
their needs; a survey with levels was essential. The physical
features of the country, including hills and valleys, river crossings,
and the nature of the ground and subsoil, would also affect the
choice of route. For this there was available a considerable
body of knowledge and experience that railway surveyors could
draw upon, much of it accumulated in the previous half-century
of canal-building and turnpike road improvement. The task
was further complicated however, by the fact that it was essential
to plan the route in relation to land ownership as well as topo-
graphy, because even the reformed Parliament was still heavily
representative of the landowning interest.

Brunel and Townsend set out from Bristol on 9 March 1833,
two days after their appointment by the Provisional Committee,
and began by going along the line of the Coalpit Heath Tramway. This led them north-eastwards, away from the valley of
the Avon, and almost at once Brunel was certain this was the
wrong way, because of the hilly country that would have to be
negotiated to get to Bath. Two days later he tried a more direct
route in the Avon valley, and found what he wanted.

The next three months were crammed with activity. Besides
going over the country, there were wells to be inspected and well-
diggers to be questioned about the rock they had found when
sinking their shafts; quarries to be visited to look at rock for-
mations; and canal plans which might reveal points that could
be used as levels for reference purposes to be examined. Although
he engaged assistants, Brunel was everywhere: by coach or on
horseback each day and often well into the evening. His nights
were mostly spent at inns in the district, writing reports and
instructions, and calculating incessantly.

In carrying the line to London, Bath and Reading were two

intermediate towns which the railway could not afford to miss. Brunel was reasonably sure the Avon was his route from Bristol to Bath. At the other end, there were various possibilities from Reading to London, depending on the siting of the London terminus, but between Bath and Reading there were two major alternatives. The southern one followed the valley of the River Kennet westwards through Newbury, south of the Marlborough Downs, into the Vale of Pewsey, and thence over into the basin of the Avon, and on to Bath – the route of the Kennet and Avon Canal. The other was north of the Marlborough Downs, first following the valley of the Thames and then the Vale of the White Horse which would be left at its head near Swindon. The route would run down into the valley of the Avon leaving it where the river makes its southward bend to Bradford-on-Avon, in favour of a more direct line through Box to Bath.

Both these routes involved a climb over the high ground between the Thames and Avon valleys. In the south this involved a summit for the line at about the 500-foot level, but in the north the crossing from the Vale of the White Horse to the Avon valley is about 200 feet lower. Brunel first looked at the southern route, but its higher summit persuaded him to favour the northern route, especially as he also had at the back of his mind the instructions about the Gloucester and South Wales areas, which could be reached more easily from it, and he recommended it to the committee in June, 1833. They then decided that the time was ripe to put the scheme before the public in Bristol, and on the 30 July there was a public meeting there, at which Brunel spoke. The next task was to establish a base of support in London.

This was a momentous step, because the scheme had so far been very much a Bristol affair. Brunel had warned the committee not to be too hasty in presenting their scheme to a wider public, and, in particular, not to make any public appearance in London until the moment was judged right. George Gibbs, one of the earliest of the Bristol men concerned with the railway, had a cousin, George Henry Gibbs, who was a London banker who had already mentioned the project to some other London businessmen. Representatives of Bristol and London first came together at Gibbs' London office on 22 August 1833. At a further meeting on 27 August, Brunel was first introduced to Charles

Alexander Saunders, newly appointed secretary to the London committee, and their friendship was immediate and remained unbroken. Brunel's need of someone who would 'give them [the Committee] a little life and sense' was more than filled by Saunders. At that meeting the name Great Western Railway was first used. It seems so characteristic of Brunel's bounding imagination that, in the absence of any other claimant, he should be given credit for it.

There were two things to be done before approaching Parliament. One was a detailed survey, primarily Brunel's task, and the other was to obtain promises of the money necessary to build and equip the line. Brunel engaged more assistants, designed and ordered his now famous travelling carriage, (a mobile drawing-office and bedroom), and rented his first London office at 53 Parliament Street. This was convenient to Parliament where he was to spend many weeks in the next two years, and from this base he set out upon the mammoth task of the detailed survey. The travelling carriage enabled Brunel to exercise continuous and detailed supervision of his assistants. The only way he could really judge their worth was by the quality of their work; by the time shortcomings came to light, too often a lot of valuable time had been lost, and much of the work had to be done again. The entries in Brunel's diary show that the hectic pace of the preliminary survey continued, with days in the open, and nights either on the road or quartered in the variable accommodation of the inns along the route. It was some compensation, perhaps that when at last he did get to bed, he was usually too tired to notice if it was comfortable or not.

The preferred route from the Thames valley to the Avon valley, going north of the Marlborough Downs, had a fairly low summit. If this could be overcome, the line could, by following the river valleys, be given gentle gradients without extensive earthworks, and Brunel could therefore concentrate on reducing sharp curvature. By comparison with the London and Birmingham line averaging 110,000 cu. yds. of earthworks per mile, the GWR required only 80,000 cu. yds., yet to this day the story persists that the fine route to Bristol was achieved by great earthworks, a symbol of Brunel's imagined scorn for anything less than the magnificent. He wanted the best; the legend is that he wanted the best regardless of expense, whereas he was satisfied with nothing that was not of the highest quality. His experiences with the Thames tunnel had shown him that 'regardless of expense' was the motto of the fool. The superb course of the line comes from the decision made about the route, rather than from a desire for engineering magnificence at any price.

Quite apart from the consideration of engineering costs, he was always alive to the need to tap as many sources of potential traffic as possible. In the 1830s the woollen cloth industry of the Cotswolds was in fatal decline due to the competition from the rise of steam-driven industry in the West Riding of Yorkshire. But the railway promoters were not insensible of the need to cater for the woollen trade. One of the few advantages of the southern alternative was that it would have served the woollen towns of Bradford-on-Avon and Trowbridge. In the end they were given a branch line. The northern route, however, allowed the possibility of an easy connexion to the northern part of the woollen district, and, probably more important, access to Gloucester and South Wales. Brunel recommended the northern line for three reasons, each of which shows how he perceived the essentials of railway success. He said: 'It offers greater facilities for constructing a railway; commands a greater revenue; and offers more of the advantages of a main trunk to the West of England than the southern one could possibly offer.' To build up a good picture of the possible revenue, Brunel also had men make surveys of the actual road traffic at Oxford, Witney, Newbury, Reading and Maidenhead.

The line as built has a gentle but virtually unbroken rise from the Thames valley to the summit level near Wootton Bassett, with the descent to the Avon valley concentrated there and down through Box tunnel. That Brunel shared the contemporary view of the hill-climbing power of the early steam locomotives is shown by the confinement of severe gradients to a short portion of the line where a stationary steam-engine equipped with rope haulage could be used to assist them. This idea was abandoned before the line was opened and for a time an assisting engine was used, but soon only the heaviest trains received even this help.

Raising the money was not easy. Parliament required that one half of the total capital should be subscribed or promised before a Railway Bill would be considered, but, despite the untiring efforts of Saunders, Brunel, and the directors, only a quarter of the £3,000,000 was sure as the latest date for deposit- a Bill in 1834 approached. Although they never changed their intention of building throughout from London to Bristol, the directors decided to apply for powers to build only the Bristol– Bath and London–Reading sections, the cost of which would be small enough to allow their promised capital to comply with the standing orders of Parliament. They hoped to have raised enough money by 1835 to apply for powers to build the Bath– Reading sections as well.

In March 1834 the great battle in Parliament began. Having passed its second reading in the House of Commons, the Bill was examined in detail by a committee of the House. Brunel was the major witness, and the lawyers of the opposition strove without success to shake him. He was quick, lucid, accurate, and restrained, and older men like George Stephenson, who had himself been through this trial, commented on his steadiness and commended his designs. Very tellingly, Stephenson, although envisaging the theoretical possibility of a better line, said in his evidence: 'I could conceive of one much superior, but I do not know so good a one existing.' Although passed by the Commons, the 1834 Bill was rejected by the House of Lords, but not, as has often been said, because of the opposition of powerful landowners. Throughout the two-year passage through Parliament, evidence constantly appears of the efforts of the directors, secretary, and engineer to avoid touching landowners' interests wherever this could be done without disabling expense, and to placate them by meeting their wishes in the most detailed way; and it paid handsomely. The 1834 Bill was rejected because although the virtue and usefulness of a London–Bristol railway had been fully established before the House of Commons, the Bill as it stood was for an incomplete work.

Having failed in 1834, the directors intended to try for the whole line in the 1835 session, and the interval was used for intesive fund-raising all over the West of England. There were numerous public meetings, generally passing a resolution in favour of the railway, and ending with an invitation to those present to subscribe for shares. As time went on, a competitor appeared in the shape of the Basing and Bath Railway, starting from a junction at Basingstoke with the London & Southampton Railway then being built, and passing south of the Marlborough

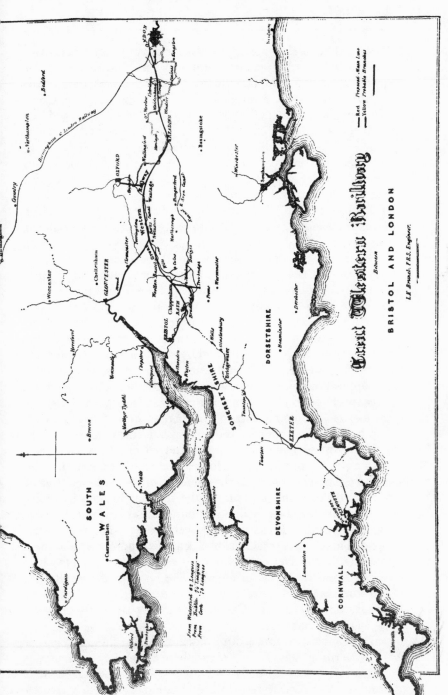

An early Prospectus map of the GWR

Downs. The Basing and Bath also held public meetings, and there is a story that at one of these Brunel, having heard the speeches of the rival promoters, so demolished them with argument that the meeting ended by supporting the Great Western. The evidence of Brunton, pioneer of 1832 and co-engineer of the Basing and Bath, suggests that the GWR party rigged the meeting, that he was unable to get a fair hearing, and that Brunel was closely involved in the episode. Considering the happenings at political meetings in those days, this is quite likely. 'Sad, harrassing work' was Saunders description of his efforts to raise capital. Nevertheless, by March 1835 two-thirds of the complete capital had been promised, and the way ahead was clear.

It was made even clearer when the House of Commons committee in 1835 accepted as already proven the need for a London–Bristol railway. From that point the battle was more with would-be competitors than with opponents of railways as such, and it was fought over details, especially the Box tunnel. In fact the word 'tunnel' seemed to stir the misgivings of the committees of both Commons and Lords. Dr. Dionysius Lardner, an all-purpose scientific pontificator of those days, was a principal opposition witness on the subject, although his oft-quoted forecast of 120 m.p.h. to be reached by an unbraked vehicle at the foot of Box incline turned out in 1835 to be a miserable 46 m.p.h. if started from rest, and 66 m.p.h. if starting at 20 m.p.h. J. U. Rastrick made it 43 m.p.h. and 48 m.p.h. respectively. Both agreed that though the high speed would be unusual, the positive danger arose from the presence of a curve a quarter of a mile beyond the bottom of the incline. Brunel, in reply, pointed out that Box incline was only half as steep as the Burlington Arcade in London, which seems to have had the desired effect. There was a great deal of talk about landowners and their interests, but in fact owners of only $23\frac{1}{2}$ miles out of $115\frac{1}{2}$ dissented from the GWR proposals. The benefits of consultation and compensation were well demonstrated, and after some seventy days before the Committees in 1835, success came on 31 August of that year.

The Committee proceedings say a lot about the approach of the governing classes to the problem of railways. Balancing the great respect accorded to private property, especially landed property, there was widespread recognition of the benefits which the railways would bring. Opposition from canal-owners and carriers, and turnpike trusts and stagecoach proprietors was heard, but had little effect on the results. Parliament knew that their business would suffer, but saw that as the penalty to be paid for being overtaken by a more advanced system. Opposition from landowners was more serious, but Brunel and his colleagues had done their work well. There was a detailed plan of the line to be built, showing where it would go and where there would be cuttings, embankments and bridges, and a Book of Reference, showing the ownership of all land over which the line would pass. Brunel called upon many of the owners to sound them out on their general attitude to the railway, and about what works would be required. We know that he personally consulted every owner whose land would have one of the dreadful tunnels under it, and his diaries record countless visits. No wonder that when he appeared before Parliamentary Committees, he was never upset on details; his courteous un-shakeability under attack came from this certainty. The opposition which carried most weight and gave most trouble was that which competed for the right to build a railway.

Before the story of construction is told, it may be timely to appraise Brunel and his view of what a railway would accomplish. From hindsight we can be fairly certain that without railways the transformation in the scale of manufacturing which is sometimes called the Factory Revolution would not have changed Victorian England as it did. The railways' contribution was the reduction of production and distribution costs, and an immense widening in the market for manufactures; their effect upon the communications of ideas was also immense. But to what extent did Brunel appreciate what was going to happen in the future?

Although the individual contribution of particular railways to economic growth has been important, the really great benefits came from the creation of a system or network of railways. It is probably no injustice to Brunel to suggest that he shared the opinion of his contemporaries about what the railways were going to do; after all he was no prophet. If we seek in his parliamentary evidence, for instance, for indications that he saw the Bristol–London line as one part of a grand design, we look in vain. He merely thought the Gloucester and South Wales traffic would be useful. But his views on, for example, a possible Exeter–Birmingham connexion, in the early 1830s show him doubting if there would be enough traffic to make it worth building. The Bristol & Exeter railway of late 1835 he welcomed as a job to be done, but he is not to be found among its progenitors. Again, in January 1835, he envisaged that Bristol might be a collecting and forwarding point for 'all the carriage of the market produce of the West of England which now finds its way eastwards from a number of different points'. He therefore found it difficult to estimate how much terminal accommodation it would be necessary to provide there. On the question of the gauge of railways he also seems to have had a view which, as more and more lines were built, looks increasingly restricted. In other words, he saw railways as offering enormous facilities wherever they existed, but does not seem at this stage to have been fully conscious of the wider implications of a national network.

Of his ideas about the impact of railways upon the ordinary people we have little conclusive evidence. At one point in his parliamentary examination, when the question arose about the demolition at Bath of some property which housed people who were not only poor but also of doubtful character, we get a glimpse of an opinion which seems entirely that of the time:

'Is it the poverty of the people you object to?'
'No, the class of people.'
'They are not merely guilty of being poor, but something else?'
'Yes.'
'Then your railway will operate as a great moral improver in the City of Bath.'

In fairness to Brunel, it must be borne in mind that the number of people who welcomed railways at all was only then starting to grow markedly. On one point Brunel seems ahead of his contemporaries: in seeing clearly that railways would have a great contribution to make to improving communications, and that speed would be of the essence in this change. He saw from the first that the Great Western must aim at a higher speed than the 20 m.p.h. average which most people concerned with railways in the 1830s considered appropriate, and his line was well suited to such higher speeds.

In civil engineering Brunel shared with Robert Stephenson

the leadership of the profession at its most advanced; as a bridge-builder probably Stephenson alone was Brunel's equal. At that time, mechanical engineering did not exist as a separate profession, but there were men whose greater practical experience in the design and maintenance of steam machinery placed them ahead of Brunel, especially where railway engines were concerned. Practical experience was what Brunel lacked in this area, but he had no shortage of it where civil engineering construction was afoot. He was soon to need it all.

5   Building the Great Western

The next few years were the busiest period of Isambard Brunel's life and, in order to avoid confusion, the undertaking which occupied most of his time – the construction of the Great Western Railway between London and Bristol – will be dealt with in this chapter. At the same time he was revolutionizing ocean steam shipping, starting work on the Clifton bridge, and getting married. But the Great Western Railway had to come first.

John Latimer, in his *Annals of Bristol* of 1887, refers to 'the deplorable error of the original railway board in neglecting the sober-minded, practical, and economical engineers of the north, and in preferring to them an inexperienced theorist, enamoured of novelty, prone to seek for difficulties rather than to evade them, and utterly indifferent as to the outlay which his reckless-ness entailed upon his employers.' Just what grudge Latimer had against Brunel is not clear, but he wrote a good deal more in the same vein. Yet, at every turn, where there is some novelty to be explained, Brunel gave his reasons in detail for preferring a particular design or course of action. The most usual reason was to get the best value for money, and, as he said in a letter to a Liverpool acquaintance who was worried about the cost of the GWR: 'We look sharper about money than you suppose – though perhaps we don't talk so much about it down here as you do up north.' If it seems like special pleading to say that, when things turned out badly, the cause of the trouble can often be traced to departure from the plan Brunel laid down, let the facts speak for themselves. It is true that with the benefits of hindsight, we can see that some of his designs were at best going to be difficult, and at worst well-nigh impossible given the materials then at hand, as witness the Gaz engine. But we look in vain for serious flaws in his reasoning. In his lifetime and after Brunel has often been attacked in terms similar to Latimer's, and above all he has been branded as a theorist, lacking practical experience. Yet there can have been few men at that time who wished so ardently to leave as little to chance as possible, and laid their plans accordingly.

The interval between the GWR Bills of 1834 and 1835 had been used, not only for securing support and funds, but also for intensive design work. Before examining the story of construction, it will be useful to see exactly how the work was to be organized. Unlike the Thames tunnel, the GWR was to be built by contractors, and Brunel's task was closely related to theirs and involved a lot of detailed work. Firstly, before the various persons or organizations were invited to submit tenders for the separate sections of the line, the railway company had to design what it wanted, and these designs were the responsibility of the railway's engineer and his assistants. It was also necessary to see that the contractor was competent to do the work for which he had contracted. This was a difficult task because, with the building of railways only then beginning on a large scale, few contractors had had time to prove themselves. Lastly, the engineer had to see that the contractor did the work properly, which involved not only checking the facts by comparison with the plans, but also being satisfied about materials, and sometimes measuring what had been done. While work was going on, opportunities for refining and improving the design and construction would constantly be occurring, so that the detailed plans would be changed while things were progressing, and prices would have to be agreed for these changes.

One of the most intractable problems in all great undertakings is that of the time factor, and progress, method, and cost were repeatedly affected by problems of timing. In preparing the designs and dealing with the details of construction, the work done between the Bills was to prove of great value, and nowhere was this more true than with regard to Brunel's detailed knowledge of what he required. In the years that followed 1835, the intensive work between the parliamentary battles paid handsome dividends.

The original survey had been made with the help of several assistants, and as soon as the Bill was passed, detailed design work began in earnest, so that tenders could be obtained and contracts assigned. A permanent staff of assistants was required, and one of the difficulties was to sort out the right men for the job. Even Marc Brunel, still awaiting from the Government the money for completing the Thames tunnel, was pressed into service to

design the arches which one of the plans for the London end
(subsequently abandoned) would require. One assistant, T.
Clark, has left us this note, addressed to Isambard's son:

I made your father's acquaintance, rather characteristically, in an
unfinished tunnel[1] of the Coalpit Heath Railway; and when the shaft
in which we were suspended cracked, and seemed about to give way,
I well remember the coolness with which he insisted upon completing
the observations he came to make.

Some of the assistants passed rapidly into and out of Brunel's
service; others prospered by their ability and rose in the world.
Brunel's view of his relationship with his assistants and his
responsibility to the directors is reflected in a letter to one of his
best assistants, William Glennie: 'My responsibility is too great
to allow of my retaining for one moment from any personal
feeling of regard the services of anyone who may appear to me
inefficient . . . and it is an understood thing that all under me are
subject to immediate dismissal at my pleasure.' As work com-
menced from both the London and Bristol ends of the line,
resident engineers in the persons of J. W. Hammond and G. E.
Frere were engaged.

It was customary, with the exception of the very largest
structures, for each contract to be for a portion of the line including both earthworks and bridges along the length. It may
help the appreciation of the problems involved if we examine
just what such operations entailed. Because of the comparatively limited – and hence restrictive – hill-climbing power of
the locomotives, the gradients of a railway (especially at that
early date) had to be much gentler than those of the hills and
valleys in its path. The hills had therefore to be cut through,
the material from the cuttings being used for embankments
across the valleys. In this way the engineer hoped to achieve a
balance of cut and fill so that he had neither a shortage of
filling material nor the problem of disposing of a surplus. In
trying to achieve this balance, he must of course have regard
to the suitability of materials from the cuttings for making the
embankments.

So much is merely a matter of comparatively simple calculation. The problem which arises in many cases relates to timing;

1. Probably Staple Hill tunnel on the Bristol & Gloucestershire Railway.

for instance, the weather may hold up the digging of cuttings or the formation of embankments. A prolonged and severe frost may make excavation almost impossible, but in Britain too much rain is the commonest cause of this difficulty. It may impede the digging of cuttings, especially as in the 1830s, without modern earth-moving equipment, the work had to be done with picks, shovels, wheelbarrows, horses, and men. Much more often it makes the excavated material so wet that when it is tipped into a valley it will not stand as an embankment, but tends to subside, which has the effect, by lessening the slope of the embankment, of using more material than planned, thus upsetting the balance of cut and fill. It also increases the ground area of the base of the embankment, and if this happens, a wider strip of land than that which has been bought for the base of the embankment may be required. Just as these troubles afflicted the railway builders in the past, so they afflict the motorway builders of today.

Another cause of lost time is difficulty in agreeing with landowners and tenants the date upon which they will hand over their land for the building work to start, an action the lawyers call 'obtaining entry'. Delay may be caused deliberately by obstinate opposition to the project, but a more frequent cause is protracted legal formalities. A special point about the dates of entry on to farming land is the understandable wish of the farmer not to give it up until his crop has been harvested. Delayed entry on to valley land can lead to cuttings being held up because there is nowhere to put the excavated soil unless land is rented for the purpose. Material so deposited will have to be handled a second time to its final resting place, and both these operations are expensive. Similarly, if a cutting cannot be started because of land entry problems, the only alternative to holding up the related embankments will be to buy material from elsewhere, a process called 'side-cutting' and 'opening up a borrow pit', and it too increases the costs.

Basically similar considerations and problems arising from timing, apply to contracts for structures. As T. Clark wrote:

Everything for which Brunel was responsible he insisted upon doing for himself. I doubt whether he ever signed a professional report that was not entirely his own composition; and every structure upon the Great Western, from the smallest culvert up to the Brent viaduct and Maidenhead bridge was entirely, in all its details, from his own designs.

That avoided the problem of being sure that the contractors' designs were sound. It did not avoid the problem of making sure that their materials and workmanship were also sound, and that the way they carried the job forward was not such as to imperil it. Satisfaction on these points often depended upon ensuring that the contractor was not deprived of part of his contract time for doing the work, and also on ensuring that if there was a delay the time lost was not regained by shoddy methods.

When the earthworks had been completed, and the structures also were in an advanced state, there was the job of laying the actual railway. Because it replaced the rough railways or temporary ways which contractors laid down to carry soil, this is called the permanent way; at this stage in the design, Brunel introduced two decidedly novel features. The early railways carried greater weights at higher speeds than any previous form of land transport, and engineers were at great pains to ensure that their track was able to take these substantial strains. As well, therefore, as requiring an easily curved and graded line, they also worked for the maximum strength and stiffness of their track. The length of rails was limited by the techniques in the ironworks of the time, although under the stimulus of engineering demand, those techniques were improving rapidly. The method of supporting the rails commonly adopted was to use large stone blocks laid in crushed stone ballast, with the rails pegged into them. On his earliest recorded railway journey, on the Liverpool and Manchester in 1831, Brunel was concerned at the bumping and jolting of the ride. It was, in his view, at least partly due to the difficulty of ensuring that the two rails were laid exactly parallel.

Considerations of the cost and durability of rails influenced Brunel in designing his permanent way, because the earlier superiority of wrought iron rails seemed to be questionable. Their faults might be caused by production defects, consequent upon the need to gain strength by rolling rails of increasingly heavier section, which were also dearer. The solution was typical Brunel: it was one which preserved an accurate gauge and a rigid way, yet allowed him to use wrought iron rails of lighter section which would be cheaper and more dependable. This was achieved by designing rails of an arch section – 'bridge rails' – which would thus be strong from form rather than mass. These were laid on a continuous line of 30-foot timbers, the two lines of which were joined together at intervals to preserve the gauge. In order to get a rigid foundation, it was intended to pack gravel hard under the longitudinals supporting the rails, and to prevent the timber and rail framework which was created from bouncing up and down on top of this gravel packing, the 'framework' was 'nailed' down into the ground with 15-foot wooden piles at intervals. In country with chalk or other rock underlying the track, Brunel proposed to use iron rods as 'nails'.

The other novelty was the adoption from the beginning of a distance between the two rails, or gauge, of seven feet, instead of the narrower gauge of 4ft. 8½in. to which the north of England lines, then approaching London, had been built. The narrower gauge, in the absence of any other evidence, is believed to have originated from that of the eighteenth-century colliery lines in the north-east. It was adopted by George Stephenson for the Stockton and Darlington, and Liverpool and Manchester Railways, and from there it spread. Brunel, however, characteristically gave thought only to what would be the best gauge for *his* railway.

The line as conceived from the beginning was to be one where speeds would be higher than the 'coal-train jog-trot', and its alignment and gradients were a reflection of this conception, as was the novel form of permanent way. The easy gradients and curves also meant that the other component of the resistance to motion, the friction between wheel and rail and between axle and journal, would be more than normally significant. In order to preserve the size and carrying capacity of the carriages and wagons and at the same time to reduce this friction, Brunel stipulated a gauge wide enough for average-sized vehicle bodies to be used which could run inside, rather than project over, the wheels. These wheels could be of a greater diameter than usual and so diminish the frictional forces. Seven feet between the rails would do it, and also allow larger engines to be used, giving greater power and speed.

'I shall not attempt to argue', wrote Brunel, 'with those who consider any increase of speed unnecessary. The public will always prefer that conveyance which is the most perfect, and speed, within reasonable limits, is a material ingredient in perfection in travelling.'

Both the novel permanent way and the novel gauge, were accepted by the boards of directors (in London and in Bristol) in 1835. We know the reasons for these novelties because we have

Brunel's case, as submitted to his directors, although just how well equipped they were to judge these matters is open to question. The logic and clarity of Brunel's arguments, however, stamp him as far superior to his contemporaries in the quality of their advocacy.

While the line from Bristol to the outskirts of London had been in dispute only as to whether the route should be north or south of the Marlborough Downs, the approach to the capital had caused a lot of argument. At one stage the directors thought of avoiding trouble in west London by joining up with the London & Birmingham Railway a few miles out of Euston and sharing that station. For various reasons this came to nothing, and a further Act of Parliament in 1837 authorized the present route into Paddington, and work on the first major structure out of London, the viaduct over the Brent valley, began in February 1836. A few months later most of the section between Paddington and Taplow, on the London side of the Thames opposite Maidenhead, was begun. Despite the fact that entry on to some of the land was held up until the Act authorizing the extension to Paddington was obtained in July 1837, the London directors hoped to open the line from Paddington to Taplow in November of that year. It was an altogether more difficult task on the Bristol to Bath section, where there were a number of tunnels to be driven. At the London end, the time factor was already beginning to cause anxiety, because, quite apart from the late start on the Paddington extension, there were delays in the delivery of timber and rails, increasing the need for close supervision of the laying of the permanent way, if expensive mistakes, which there would be no time to put right, were to be avoided.

In June 1836 Brunel was considering the company's need for locomotives, and he sent out a circular letter to the leading engine-builders of the day. It contained some engineering design limits which were quite within Brunel's field, and one at least that was not. This concerned the maximum speed of the piston in the cylinder, because Brunel had decided 'that a certain velocity of piston [is] found most advantageous'. He wished 30 m.p.h. to be attained at this 'most advantageous' piston speed, while stipulating also maximum boiler pressure, and engine weight. Within these limits, which even in 1836 were extremely conservative, he left the designers to their own devices, but the piston speed criterion was destined to cause some unlikely and quite useless designs for the GWR. In order to keep the speed of their pistons in the cylinder down to Brunel's limit, the various designers had to use extremely large driving wheels for their engines, or gear them up, and the effect of either was seriously to reduce their hauling power. Large wheels also cramped the boiler, adding to the mischief.

A superintendent of locomotives was also required, and in 1837 Brunel was approached by Daniel Gooch of Bedlington, Northumberland, very much in the heart of the George Stephenson country. Gooch's introduction to iron-founding and engineering had been with the rail pioneer, Birkinshaw, and subsequently he had been at the new Vulcan Foundry, a Lancashire locomotive works, and with Robert Stephenson & Co., probably the most advanced locomotive-builders in the world. In 1837 he was working with his brother constructing the Manchester & Leeds Railway. His varied experience in locomotive-building offset in Brunel's opinion, his youth. So Gooch joined Brunel in August of that year, and began to make a temporary locomotive depot ready at West Drayton. The engines came by sea to London, and thence by canal to West Drayton, and the first arrived in November, 1837. Happily – even providentially – the GWR had also acquired from Robert Stephenson & Co. an engine which had been built for an overseas railway and left on their hands when the financial crisis of 1836 overwhelmed their customer. It was not therefore built to Brunel's conditions, and was much more normal. Altered to the broad gauge and named *North Star*, it arrived in 1837 soon after the first of the engines built under the 'Brunel conditions', which turned out to be a collection of unreliable freaks. Unfortunately, *North Star* was delivered to then railless Taplow, and so could not be used to help the contractors. From the beginning Gooch had his hands full keeping the engines delivered to West Drayton in working order.

At the end of 1837 the building of the line was going on at a great rate, but November came and went without any opening to the public, and only in February 1838 were the difficulties of the supply of timber and rails overcome. Brunel was of course extremely busy, but an accident in his first steamship, the *Great Western*, in April 1838, prevented his superintendence of the hurried laying of quite a lot of the newly-arrived rails. However, on 31 May the proprietors made a ceremonial first trip (behind the ever-reliable *North Star*) to Taplow and back. The official GWR history records that 'a Bristol Director, T. R. Guppy, distinguished himself by walking along the tops of the carriages from one end of the train to the other whilst it was going at full speed, doubtless on the return journey after luncheon.' Five days later the line was opened to the public, and their troubles began almost immediately. The Great Western Railway, alas, failed to live up to the promises of the engineer and the hopes of the owners. The riding of the carriages, though no worse than on the London & Birmingham line, was decidedly rough: the engines were keeping Gooch more than busy. 'I had to begin in a measure to rebuild one half of the stock I had to work with', he wrote. 'For many weeks my nights were spent in a carriage in the engine-house at Paddington, as repairs had to be done to the engines at night to get them to do their work next day.'

The price of the shares fell, and the directors were anxious to find out what was wrong and to put it right. North country shareholders, especially in the Liverpool area, had never shared the directors' confidence in Brunel and his novelties, and they were certain to make trouble.

Although Gooch's efforts slowly improved the engine situation, and the carriage springing was also put right, it became obvious that the permanent way was the main cause of the trouble. The ballast under the continuous longitudinal timbers which supported the rails had not been solidly enough packed down. As a result the timbers sagged a little between the piles which were supposed to hold them firmly down. This trouble was due principally to the delays that had been experienced in obtaining timber and the difficulties of impregnating it with preservative chemicals, and to the late delivery of rails. Much of the permanent-way work had therefore been done in a hurry.

To attribute this bad workmanship to Brunel's enforced absence because of his accident would imply grave criticism of Hammond, the resident engineer at the London end. How Brunel dealt with this personal point in his report of August 1838 to the directors tells us a lot about him as 'a man under authority':

'It became necessary', he said 'at last to force forward the work more rapidly than was at all consistent with due care in the execution; and during the whole of this period I was most unfortunately prevented by a serious accident from even seeing the work almost until the day of opening, when I ought to have personally superintended the whole. I do not mean that the work was neglected by those whose duty it was to supply my place – far from it; but in such a case a new work cannot be properly directed except under the eye of the master.'

Hammond, described in 1836 by Brunel as 'a good fellow and very useful', could not have asked for a better chief than the one who was prepared so elegantly yet decidedly to take the blame on his own shoulders.

Brunel also came under fire because of the inadequacy of the locomotives, and their unreliability. He justified his criteria by pointing out that the principal proportions of the engines were those which had been recommended by the most able experimentalists and writers, and adopted by the most experienced makers. In that none of the locomotive-builders pointed out the defects which would and did ensue from his conditions, his justification is valid. But he was certainly ill-informed on the consensus of opinion about the material dimensions of locomotives which experience had forced upon locomotive-builders; nor had he examined in detail whether successful engines of the late 1830s accorded with them. The great trouble came from the limitations on weight and piston speed, which virtually ensured that the engines would be both 'under-boilered' and 'over-geared' by having small boilers for lightness, and very large driving wheels to reduce the piston speed.

The criticism of Brunel's locomotive design overflowed on to Gooch whom the directors thought not up to his job, and he was called upon to report on the state of his sub-department. Although it is obvious that a lot of his troubles came directly from Brunel's design criteria for the engines, Gooch's report on them individually did not implicate Brunel. Most of the defects he equated with bad workmanship. The failings of the locomotives and the rough riding of the trains were considered by those opposed to Brunel to be the result of the broad gauge, and upon this point they concentrated their attack. How much of it was in fact an attempt to establish the 'Liverpool Party' on the board of directors is a matter for conjecture; the broad gauge was their excuse for a full scale onslaught. The use of the word 'party' suggests a parallel with politics, and it is a reminder of how close was the involvement of the directors with their undertaking; it was a conflict in which personal feelings were as important as commercial success.

At no time did Brunel attempt to deny that things were far from well with their railway, and he eventually suggested that other engineers should be called in by the board for an independent report. This was done and while Nicholas Wood and John Hawkshaw were each looking over the line, Brunel presented a defence of his theory and practice to the August meeting of shareholders. He was not driven out, but the opposition was clearly waiting for Wood and Hawkshaw to make the ammunition for them to fire at Brunel and the directors. Brunel had by this time come to the conclusion that in making the rest of the line, the cost of driving the piles would be better spent in using bigger timbers, and heavier rails. He defended his gauge with skill, reiterating its advantages in detail, and rebutting criticisms decisively. He did not lack supporters, and among them were Saunders, the company secretary, George Henry Gibbs, one of the leading London directors, and Charles Russell, M.P. Brunel's friend Roch, however, had already retired from the Bristol committee. He reappeared in the 1840s when Brunel discovered to his dismay that the South Wales Railway was planned to go through Roch's home, a disaster which happily was avoided.

Wood's and Hawkshaw's reports were received by the end of 1838, and neither the board nor their attackers got much comfort from them because they were so inconclusive. Hawkshaw merely condemned the permanent way as unnecessarily complicated and expensive, without really saying where he thought Brunel was in error. He did however put his finger firmly on one point about the seven-foot gauge. He foresaw that this gauge would isolate the Great Western, and that while he could not show that it was disadvantageous to them as a matter of engineering, he felt it would be a great commercial liability. Brunel's reply to this, the most damaging argument in the long run, was that the Great Western commanded a district in which there were no other railways. As long as the standard of its service to the public was high, its monopoly would be unchallenged, and its gauge would be no great hindrance. With another powerful railway, the London & Southampton, already in existence along part of their southern flank, this reply seems curiously blinkered.

Nicholas Wood's report came to no useful conclusion either,

though the inescapable Dr. Dionysius Lardner's trials had indicated that the locomotives were not very much use, being weak, slow and extravagant users of coke. Brunel and Gooch altered that radically, in time for the crucial meeting on 9 January 1839 when there was a noticeable faintness of heart among the directors who were mostly ready to abandon their engineer. However, Brunel fought well, though not intemperately. He was always ready to acknowledge his mistakes, and his steadfast support of Gooch must also have owed something to the fact that Brunel himself had come to realize his errors over the locomotive designs. Moreover, the improvements to *North Star*, which were kept a secret from 'the enemy', so drastically improved its performance that the directors took heart. Much of their weakness, perhaps, stemmed from fear of being taken over by the Liverpool party, but in the event they put a bold face on the matter, and, as Gibbs said after their victory, 'We had secured their respect, kept them out of the Direction, retained our Engineer, and preserved our gauge.' The order in which he put those four victories suggests something of the flavour of the contest. Brunel, as well as the board, was victorious, though there had been a point at which even his confidence in himself had wavered.

One of the miscellaneous weapons with which Brunel's opponents belaboured him was a rumour about the failure of his great bridge over the Thames at Maidenhead, which would carry the line on from Taplow. It was in brick, and a triumph of design because the arches were so flat. As is usual practice, false arches of wood, called centerings, were made, and the brick arches constructed on top of them. The contractor, who had not believed Brunel's bridge would stand until its designer proved it to him by geometry, then went to the other extreme and rashly eased these centerings away from the brick arches before the mortar had set, causing some distortion of the eastern arch. This was hailed as another result of Brunel's dangerous novelties, but in fact, after the centerings were replaced and repairs effected, the bridge stood firm, as it still does. When a storm blew the replaced centerings away, Brunel was able to say disarmingly that they had actually been eased some months before. In 1893, an identical bridge was built parallel with the original to carry extra lines when the railway was quadrupled.

Work to the west of the bridge had started before the first

section of line was opened, including the two-mile Sonning
Cutting, which proved to be too much for Ranger, the contractor.
It was taken out of his hands and given to others in part, the
GWR doing some of it themselves. The track, however, was of the
new pattern with heavier rails and timbers, without piles, and
this section of the line ran to Reading where Brunel's fresh
approach to any problem produced yet another novelty.

As most of Reading was then south of the line, he overcame the
problem that London-bound passengers would have in some
manner to cross the westbound (or down) line to reach the up
line by building two stations, both south of the line. One was for
up trains which therefore twice crossed the path of down trains;
the latter had a straight run [Plate 12]. Remembering the
primitive signalling and brakes of the time, it seems a dangerous
arrangement, but several other stations were built in later years
to the same pattern. They were a nuisance to traffic for years,
and Brunel really should have known better.

At the Bristol end, work had started simultaneously with the
London end, and there was much to do. The Avon had to be
bridged several times; there were five tunnels; and Bristol and
Bath stations were to be built on arches. Mr Ranger, the contractor for Sonning Cutting, was involved, and here also he
failed, perhaps because he had taken on too much. As the works
were so complicated, the need to supersede Ranger had a most
seriously delaying effect. Unlike the severe winter of 1837–8
when frost had 'paralysed the exertions of the Engineer', the
trouble in 1839–40 was rain and floods. When the dry weather
again returned, the work was pressed on, and the Bristol to Bath
section was opened on 31 August 1840. It is said that the last rail
into Bristol was laid less than an hour before. By that time the
London end of the line had reached 63½ miles towards Bristol.

On the intervening stretch to Bath, work was of course
proceeding, with Brunel as usual so busy that he seemed to be
everywhere at once. Early on 25 October 1840, he witnessed his
first major railway accident, while waiting on the platform at
Faringdon Road Station (later called Challow), then temporarily
the end of the line. The night goods train was heard as Brunel and
others waited, and it became apparent that the train was not
slowing down. Great Western commercial policy at that time
was such that behind the tender of the engine an *open truck*
contained the guard and three goods-train passengers (the

equivalent of third class), whose custom was not to be encouraged. Without stopping, the train passed through the station and the temporary engine-shed beyond, where the rails ended, and it crashed, killing the driver, who seems to have been asleep on his feet. The engine was called *Fire King* and was one of Gooch's first designs, to assist *North Star* and replace the faulty ones made to Brunel's specification.

In connecting the two ends of the line, the major remaining work was Box Tunnel. Unlike the Kilsby Tunnel on the London & Birmingham Railway, which was the only one of comparable size, water was not a major problem, though there was some to be dealt with. Numerous shafts were sunk from the surface, and tunnelling was carried on from each, eventually joining up to form 1¾ miles under the oolite. So stable was the rock that there was no need for brickwork tunnel lining at the eastern end. In its day, it was the longest tunnel in the world.

While London and Bristol were not joined together by railway, the Bristol committee enjoyed considerable independence, as evidenced by the rather more elaborate finish given to things like stations and tunnel mouths at their end of the line. Many of the tunnel fronts were turretted, or had other affinities with castles. One front, which was partly demolished by a slip of earth, appealed to the romantic in Brunel, who left it unfinished and planted ivy round it, because he said it reminded him of a medieval ruin. The Box tunnel was, however, in the classical style. Bristol station was built in the Tudor Gothic style inside and out. The frontage has battlements and turrets, while within, the original station with its wooden hammer-beam roof has still just escaped the reforming hand of the twentieth century. This style of roof was necessary because the station was built on arches, and the use of these cantilever timbers prevented thrust against the side walls, which merely held down the tails of the cantilevers.

The lavish artistic proclivities of the Bristol committee called forth remonstrance from London, and by the time the line was opened throughout on 30 June 1841, the proud proprietors had spent more than double the estimate of something under £3,000,000 given in the prospectus of 1834. By mid-1838 the cost, without engines and other rolling stock, was over £4,500,000, and £6,282,000 had been spent by the end of 1841. The line into Paddington had been expensive, but the costs of delays due to weather had been more so. At one stage they had to dredge the Thames near Goring for ballast, as the ground they had bought to provide it was flooded. Work done in a hurry to make up for lost time was also bound to be more expensive, and Brunel's reports are full of references to side-cutting to provide material for embankments.

Gooch had drawn attention to a possible lack of water and mentioned the possibility of recouping some of their losses by turning these side-cuttings into reservoirs when proposing Swindon as 'the best site for our principal engine establishment'. This would be needed because already the Bristol & Exeter and the Cheltenham & Great Western Union Railways were coming into being, to be leased and worked by the GWR. In order to ease the burden on the hard-pressed capital account, the directors came to an unusual arrangement with Messrs. Rigby, who had already built many of the original stations. At Swindon, Rigbys were to provide a station, refreshment-rooms, and cottages for the GWR employees, all without charge. The GWR provided the land, and paid rent for the cottages, which they recovered from their tenants. Rigby's main source of income from this deal was the refreshment-room profits, and to make sure of these all regular trains were required to stop for at least ten minutes at Swindon, an incubus which remained until 1895 when it was removed by the payment of £100,000 compensation.

Isambard Brunel's great work was not finished before other railways came under his hand, of which the Bristol & Exeter and Cheltenham & Great Western Union have already been mentioned. He remained the GWR engineer until his death, and was of course constantly travelling upon it and dealing with its affairs. There is a note to Gooch in the early 1840s concerning the state of some of the carriages, in which Brunel says that at that time he 'makes it a rule always to try each carriage in the trains I travel by'. This conjures up a picture of Brunel running smartly at each station from one carriage to the next, including the third class ones!

6   Irons in the Fire

At the end of 1835, when the GWR contests in Parliament had been won, Brunel moved to 18 Duke Street, overlooking St. James's Park, and it was a moment in which he reflected upon what he called his 'irons', the projects with which he was concerned. Naturally he could not think about the way success had come without wondering how long it would last, and what fate held in store. The reverses of his life until the golden promise of the GWR, had emphasized how easy it would be to fall as swiftly as he had risen to success, but introspection did not get the upper hand on that occasion, and his thoughts turned instead to marriage. In his diary he speculates: 'Mrs B. – I forsee one thing – this time 12 months I shall be a married man. How will that be? Will it make me happier?' In view of the immense amount of work and travelling he was doing, it is difficult to imagine how he found time for courtship and marriage.

Benjamin and William Hawes, friends from his Thames tunnel days, introduced him to the Horsley family who lived at what is now 128 Church Street, Kensington. They were an extremely talented group, and both music and the visual arts flourished among them. Isambard found this circle of cultured and sociable people easy and delightful, and as 128 Church Street welcomed Mendelssohn, Clara Schumann, and Joseph Joachim during these years, he was far from being the outstanding figure in the circle. He soon formed a lifelong friendship with the elder son, John who was an accomplished artist. Horsley made some notable portraits of Brunel, and became a Royal Academician. He was also interested in design, as well as being an illustrator of children's books and the producer of the very first Christmas card in 1845. Brunel also found the company of the younger daughters, Fanny and Sophy, most agreeable. However, it was upon Mary, the Horsley's eldest girl, that his attention was fixed almost from first acquaintance, and, during a long, leisurely walk on a Sunday evening in May 1836, he proposed to her and was accepted. He confessed that he had loved and admired her for a long time, but had nevertheless determined to leave her free until he had risen sufficiently in the world to be able to keep her in comfort, and he felt that that time had now come.

Isambard's long acceptance as a friend of the family made it obvious that he would be welcomed as a member of it. The usual conferences between the families passed off well, and, as GWR matters were pressing, there was little delay before the marriage on 5 July 1836. The honeymoon through North Wales, south to Devon and thence home, was characteristically punctuated by a meeting with the GWR secretary, Saunders, at Cheltenham. Business was never far away, though Saunders also brought letters of a more domestic kind from the Horsley family.

When the Brunels came home at last to 18 Duke Street, Mary found that there were many things to fill her husband's days, besides the business of setting up home. Happily his GWR reputation, as yet unclouded by the troubles and disputes of the gauge question, was bringing in plenty of work from other associated interests, and funds for making a home were not short. At this time, as his diary recorded, everything seemed to be going his way. The first entry in his 'list of irons' at the end of 1835 is: 'Clifton Bridge – my first child, my darling, is actually going on – recommenced week last Monday – Glorious! ! '

In 1836 the British Association for the Advancement of Science held its annual meeting in Bristol, and, on 27 August, the Marquis of Northampton laid the first stone of the bridge abutment on the Leigh Woods side. On that occasion it was hoped that the money raised from all sources would be sufficient to carry the work through.

At the commencement of the work it was necessary to provide some means of transferring materials and light equipment from one side of the gorge to the other. For this purpose Brunel caused a bar, 1,000 feet long, to be made by welding together short lengths of 2-inch wrought iron, hauling one end across the gorge as the welders added sections. Just before the gap had been spanned, the end of the bar broke away and it fell across the river. The result was a pronounced kink near the half-way mark, accentuating the sag produced by its weight. When it was in place, one of his assistants made an unauthorized trial trip which nearly ended in tragedy. The wheels of a cradle ran on the bar, and a basket hung below it, and, during this first crossing the cradle stuck at the kink, to the dismay of its foolhardy passenger. To make matters worse, the mast of a passing ship caught one hanging loop of the hauling rope, but a quick slash with a knife averted that disaster, and the basket was at length hauled back to safety. The passenger's troubles, however, were not over; a wrathful Brunel had still to be faced.

Although a new bar replaced the one with the kink, the cradle still displayed a tendency to get stuck at the bottom of the arc, as it did on 27 September. Brunel had invited his wife to accompany him on the first crossing, but Mary did not fancy such an aerial excursion, so he took with him a boy named Claxton (it is not known whether he was related to Brunel's staunch friend, Christopher Claxton, R.N.). They had an eventful trip, as the cradle became stuck, and Isambard alarmed those watching by swarming up the ropes from the basket to the cradle, freeing it, climbing down again into the basket, and giving the signal for hauling to continue.

Let us now leave bridges and railways, and trace Brunel's association with the sea, for Bristol was to be not only the birthplace of his bridge and his railway, but also the home of his ship. It will be remembered that the original GWR Bill had to be modified by leaving out the Reading–Bath section, because of lack of money, and that this incompleteness defeated the promoters in Parliament in 1834, although the Bill for the complete 118 miles was successfully promoted in the next year. Nevertheless, some of the directors seemed to have been apprehensive about the size of the undertaking. At a board meeting in October 1835, a remark betraying something of this anxiety provoked Isambard to reply, 'Why not make it longer, and have a steamboat to go from Bristol to New York, and call it the *Great Western?*' 'By God, the young fellow will be taking us to the moon next!' somebody was heard to reply, and he probably would, too, had he been able. Exactly what prompted Brunel to make the suggestion of a steamship connecting the railway is not clear. There is no evidence that he had been speculating about the possibility and was only waiting for an opportunity to launch his idea. Yet it would not be at all typical of him to make his remark on the spur of the moment, without prior thought. Whatever the reason, it opened a new era in ocean transport.

As early as 1819 a ship with a steam-engine installed had crossed the Atlantic, but to call this pioneering voyage of the

Savannah the first transatlantic navigation by steam would be an exaggeration, because she used steam only for an auxiliary engine, which was worked for only $3\frac{1}{2}$ days out of $27\frac{1}{2}$. Other early crossings were of a similar nature, and the ocean still awaited the first voyage completely under steam. In the opinion of many of the people well qualified to judge, believing such a voyage impossible, it would wait forever. Marc Brunel himself was at one time of the opinion 'that steam cannot do for distant navigation', a view based on experience of the voracious coal-devouring habits of the steam-engines of the 1820s.

At some stage in his career before the GWR project – perhaps in the lean years of the early 1830s – Isambard had been reflecting on this aspect of steam navigation. His thinking brought to him the realization that the view, firmly based as it was on contemporary experience, might be wrong in theory. Obviously the longer the voyage, the more coal would have to be carried, and this would have one of two effects: either it would reduce the ship's capacity to carry other things, or it would have to be a bigger ship to support the cargo-carrying capacity of its holds. The former effect would seriously impair the ship's economic usefulness, perhaps to the point of making it an impossible financial proposition. The alternative of having a bigger ship to maintain the cargo capacity appeared equally pointless, because a bigger ship would need more power to drive it through the water, necessitating bigger engines and still greater coal consumption. Using either of these alternatives, it was in theory possible to calculate the maximum voyage that could be made in safety without re-coaling, and that distance was notably short of transatlantic crossing. At some stage, Isambard came to see the flaw in these arguments, and what he did as a result was one of his greatest contributions to the development of communications.

The capacity of a ship to carry a load is determined by the three dimensions of length, breadth, and depth or draught. The resistances which must be overcome to move the ship are those offered by the water and the wind, of which the former is by far the more important. Thinking about what actually happens as a ship moves caused Brunel to realise that: 'The resistance of vessels in the water does not increase in direct proportion to their tonnage. This is easily explained; the tonnage increases as the cubes of their dimensions, while the resistance increases about as their squares; so that a vessel of double the tonnage of another, capable of containing an engine of twice the power, does not really meet with double the resistance. Speed will therefore be greater with the large vessel, or the proportionate power of the engine and consumption of fuel may be reduced.' The 'more coal – bigger ship – more power – more coal' connexion, which seemed to preclude ocean voyages beyond a certain distance, was theoretically incorrect.

The passage quoted above was inserted by Brunel into a report in 1835, which had been prepared by his friend, Christopher Claxton, and T. R. Guppy, whom we last met walking on the roof of the first GWR train. Guppy was a man of great diversity of interest and learning, and had taken up Brunel's remark about a steamship to New York, after the GWR board meeting. Brunel was so confident of the soundness of his theoretical calculations that Guppy and others proceeded with the idea of transatlantic navigation. At the beginning of 1836 a company was formed, called the Great Western Steamship Company, and Claxton, Guppy, and Brunel formed the 'Building Committee'.

Before the history of Brunel's first two ships is recorded, a question remains to be answered. How serious was he, at that GWR board meeting, in suggesting an extension of the railway across the Atlantic? Such evidence as there is seems to point away from a desire on his part to encompass both railways and transatlantic steamships in one company. Yet, in view of the interest we know he had taken in the long distance steamship question, his remark was almost certainly more than just a joke. The position may be summed up thus: he wanted to see his theories put to the test because transocean steamships presented a technical and scientific challenge. He realized the way in which a steamship line from Bristol to America would be the counterpart of the Great Western Railway from London to Bristol. Both would offer outstanding advances of speed and certainty, and he was sure that the public would want them, and would support them with their patronage. And perhaps he hoped that ships and trains would revive the waning prosperity of his beloved Bristol.

In 1836 his hopes for the port of Bristol and the correctness of his own calculations were put to the test. Dr. Lardner was, almost inevitably, prominent among those who condemned the attempt as doomed to failure, but despite his proof that the crossing was impossible, the *Great Western* was begun.

7   *Across the Wide Ocean*

The coming of steam-driven machinery caused the separation of the new science of mechanical engineering from the older one of civil engineering. Until the 1830s the majority of engineers would probably be sufficiently familiar with both branches to be able to combine them, but from about that date mechanical engineering became increasingly specialized, and fewer men could combine the two. Isambard Brunel's rise to fame took place just as the division was becoming manifest, and we have seen the trouble that occurred when he used his mechanical engineering knowledge to lay down design criteria for the first GWR locomotives.

In the 1830s, however, the increasing use of iron in shipbuilding brought engineering into contact with naval architecture, although the term 'marine engineering' was applied only to the business of ships' engines. The design and building of ships had always been a separate craft or profession, and it was to this specialization that Brunel turned his attention in 1836.

He did not hesitate to propose a ship of greater size than any other, because his ideas about the mechanics of ships' movement made it a case of the bigger the better. To Brunel, a ship was in essence simply a moving rather than a stationary structure, which had to survive two sets of stresses rather than only one. These were the stresses placed on the hull by the cargo and the other things inside it, especially those which, like the engines had movement of their own, and the stresses placed on it by the movements of the sea outside. Design was therefore a matter of analysing these forces and making the skeleton or frame of the ship strong enough to resist them. The result was a hull of exceptional longitudinal strength, to ensure that the external forces would not strain the structure, nor would her engines shake her to pieces, as was not uncommon in the early days of steam at sea.

The Great Western Steam-Ship Company having been formed, the construction of the hull of their first ship was entrusted to an old-established firm of Bristol shipbuilders headed by William Patterson. The ship was to be made of oak, propelled by paddles which would be driven by side-lever beam engines. Brunel did not design the engines himself, but invited the principal marine engine-builders of the day to tender for the job. The tender of Maudslays was accepted, Brunel pointing out that the cost, so long as it was reasonable, should not be the deciding factor. As there was so much dispute about the feasibility of what they were going to do, the eyes of the world would in effect be upon them. 'You will remember,' said Brunel, 'that it will be the longest voyage yet run; and that the future success of the boat as a passenger ship – nay, even of the company's boats generally, and, to a great extent the reputation of Bristol as an American steamboat station, may depend upon the success of this first voyage.' A further reason for making sure they could rely on the engines from the beginning was that there would be no opportunity for an extended trial; competitors were already in the field.

Bristol's decline as an ocean port had been matched by Liverpool's rise, and the Transatlantic Steamship Company of that town obviously did not share Dr. Lardner's views as to the impossibility of steaming across the Atlantic. A London firm was also preparing a challenge. As it seemed that neither of the challengers could be finished before Brunel's ship, both of his rivals chartered steamships built for the service between Ireland and England, and started altering them for the lengthy Atlantic crossing. The race was on, and, as the engines would have to be perfect from the start, Maudslay's decided to use the heavy but well-tried side-lever design, rather than the oscillating or 'vibrating' engine which they were then developing.

The s.s. *Great Western* was launched at Bristol in July 1837, having taken a year to build. She went then to the Thames, under sail most of the way, to be fitted with her engines, which were of 750 i.h.p. to propel her 1,340 tons. Their installation and the fitting-out of the ship developed into a race with the conversion of the *Sirius*, chartered by the British and American Steam Navigation Co., which was also taking place on the Thames.

Because the *Sirius* was only half the size of the *Great Western*, she intended to coal at Cork, and she left the Thames for New York on 28 March 1838, as the *Great Western* was just finishing her trials. Three days later, the *Great Western* left for Bristol where she would commence her maiden voyage, 'having on board Captain Claxton, Mr Guppy, Mr Brunel and many other persons interested in her success'. Two hours after leaving London, the insulation round the boilers caught fire at the point where the funnel passed through the upper deck, and both deck and the beams supporting it were soon burning. While Capt. Hosken put her hard-a-port to run aground by Canvey Island, the Chief Engineer managed to get to the boilers and turn on feed-water pumps in an effort to save them.

Claxton got through the forward boiler-room to the forward part of the ship, and tried to put the fire out with a hose. His efforts were interrupted when he was knocked down by a heavy weight falling on him through the smoke. When he picked himself up he found he had been bowled over by a man, who was now lying face down in a pool of water from the hose. Claxton shouted up to those on the forecastle for a rope to be put down through the forehatch, and had him hauled up out of danger. When Claxton and the others had brought the fire under control, he went on deck and found that it was Isambard Brunel who had fallen on him. Brunel had been climbing down the long ladder that reached from the forehatch, when he stepped on a burnt rung, fell fully eighteen feet and hit his head on some part of the ship's framing on the way down. He was lying unconscious on a sail, and as soon as possible he was sent ashore in a boat. It was this accident which kept him away from the GWR in the vital days when the track was being laid from Paddington to Taplow.

As soon as the fire was out and the tide rose again, the crew got the ship off the mud and set sail for Bristol. Bad news travelled fast, and the story of the fire caused dismay in Bristol, though this turned to joy when the *Great Western* arrived on 2 April. Six days later she left for New York, four days after the *Sirius* had left Cork.

Early in the morning of 23 April, the *Sirius* arrived in New York, and the citizens of that city welcomed her with great rejoicing, for she heralded a new era in the story of the communications between the Old World and the New. For all their differences, America and Europe had much in common; and now this, the most important of all connexions, was made less uncertain and much swifter. For this reason, New Yorkers were beside themselves when the *Great Western* arrived in the course of the same afternoon, and they transferred their admiration to the new arrival.

Brunel had been kept in bed by his fall and although he had been able to write to Claxton at Bristol about what needed attending to before the ship sailed, he had been unable to be there in person. The GWR was just approaching the crucial point of opening its first section, and this prevented him from seeing the vindication of his theory of the feasibility of long-distance navigation. The *Sirius* had only fifteen tons of coal left when she reached New York, but the *Great Western* had 200 tons.

The *Great Western*'s real rivals were the *British Queen* of the British and American Co., and the *Liverpool,* of the Transatlantic Steamship Co., which replaced the *Sirius*, and the *Royal William,* the second of the original challengers. Both these new ships were big, though smaller than the *Great Western,* which continued to be one of the finest ships on the Atlantic until 1845. She was finally broken up in 1857.

A ship to eclipse the *Great Western* was planned as soon as success was established in 1838. Having defeated his critics by the size of his first vessel – Dr. Lardner was by now modifying 'impracticable' to 'unprofitable' – Brunel proposed another ship at least double the size. When built, this pioneered two of the greatest steps forward in large ship construction since the first application of steam power: she was built of iron, and driven by a screw propeller. These innovations were very important, and they deserve closer examination because on them, in the eyes of many people, Brunel's fame as an innovator chiefly rests.

Iron had been used for some time previously in the hulls of ships, one of the earliest being a Yorkshire canal boat of 1777, and the earliest iron seagoing steamer was the *Aaron Manby* of 1821. The visit to Bristol in 1838 of one of these small pioneers, the *Rainbow* of 407 tons, brought Brunel's ideas to the point. Claxton and Patterson, the shipbuilder, went with the *Rainbow* to Antwerp to see how she behaved at sea. Obviously all went well because, by the following spring, the design for the *Great Western*'s sister ship had grown to that of an iron ship of well over 3,000 tons gross. The carrying capacity of such a ship could be much larger as she had iron frames, which would be as strong as timbers of the most enormous size. Brunel was adept at arranging the components of his structures in such a way that one stress could be made to counteract another, and, in this task of 'playing off' the forces in ship design against one another, iron was much preferable to wood, because its greater stiffness allowed the iron framing to derive strength from its form, rather than merely from its mass. (Brunel had done just this with his bridge rails on the GWR.) In a ship, the use of iron would also minimize the fire hazard, and, so great was the increasing shortage and cost of suitable timber in England, that for large ships iron was also becoming a cheaper material.

While the various plans for the hull were succeeding one another, a great deal of thought was being given to the engines, for engine design was improving rapidly at this time, both as regards economy and compactness. Maudslays were in the van of the drive for improvements. Their eventual tender exceeded by fifty per cent that of a young man named Francis Humphreys, about which Brunel had his doubts, but the Board decided, nevertheless, to use Humphrey's design. Then Halls of Dartford, who were manufacturing agents for Humphreys, pointed out that this would be a 'one-off' job, and what would now be called the development costs would have to be charged in their entirety to this engine. They suggested that the steamship company should build it themselves, and this they resolved to do as there seemed little chance of getting it made in Bristol. The sensible course would have been to have taken up Maudslays' tender, but they pressed on despite Brunel's view that, in the end, building their own engines would cost at least as much. Reading between the lines of his report one can sense that he could smell trouble and tried as tactfully as he could to warn them off, and events fell out much as he had feared.

Humphreys was grappling with the difficulties of building the engines in the company's yard at Bristol when there was yet another change of plan. This was so great an addition to his worries that Humphreys resigned, leaving the Building Committee with the whole task. Brunel had decided to abandon paddles and use the screw propeller, which meant re-aligning the crankshaft from athwartships to fore and aft, and this necessitated a complete redesigning of the engines. No wonder Humphreys resigned!

The first Englishman to have any real success with the screw propeller was Francis Pettit Smith. When in May 1840, the propeller-driven steamship *Archimedes* (which was largely an experimental vessel) called at Bristol, Guppy sailed aboard her to Liverpool. By October, Brunel was convinced that this was both a practical and an advantageous mode of propulsion. It is clear, therefore, that Brunel neither invented, nor first used, the screw propeller, but his successful use of it was the beginning of the end for paddles.

Brunel's reasons for his advocacy are on record. He first examined the *Archimedes* and its performance in detail; and the Great Western Steam-Ship Company chartered her for six months. Despite not being well-shaped and having a rather small, rough propeller, she managed to make good use of the power of her engines by comparison with paddle-steamers. Brunel, therefore, rightly reasoned that a well-made propeller, correctly proportioned and related to an appropriate hull, would show even greater benefits. His review of possible drawbacks indicates that their new ship would not need alteration because she was well adapted to take that form of propulsion. The liability of paddles to damage more than outweighed the benefits from their steadying influence, although this induced rival companies to build them for the boisterous Atlantic passage up to 1862. Opponents of the screw asked what would happen when pitching brought the stern and the propeller out of the water, but observations by Capt. Claxton's son abroad the *Great Western* and the *Archimedes* showed that for various reasons this rarely happened. There was, lastly, the problem of gearing up a slow marine engine to the revolutions needed by the propellor. Brunel experimented on this, for the gearing used in the *Archimedes* produced quite unacceptable noise and vibration.

Having dealt with the possible difficulties, he listed the advantages, which he saw as increased efficiency, better ship design and hull form, and greater reliability. The first stemmed from the relative efficiencies of the *Great Western* and the mediocre *Archimedes*. On the second point, there would be a 100-ton saving in weight and a lot more would be brought down from deck level, as in a paddle-steamer, to well below the water-line, which would increase the ship's stability. In addition, paddles required a wasp-waisted ship, and this made longitudinal strength harder to secure and generally complicated the design.

Thirdly, all paddle-ships suffered from variations in the efficiency of the paddles, because their immersion became greater as the cargo was increased, and heeling under sail caused an unequal load on the paddles. Engines driving a propeller do not suffer the shocks which occur when the waves strike paddles, and all this added up to a balance of reliability and lower running costs in favour of the screw. Brunel found the advantages of the screw 'so evident that I am disposed to apologize to you for having occupied your time in pointing them out.' The board agreed, and the stage was set for a revolution in the world of shipping.

The *Great Britain*, as she was to be named, was 322 feet long and fifty-one feet in the beam. As in the *Great Western*, Brunel concentrated on longitudinal strength, made easier by the absence of paddles. He included ten girders running the length of the ship's bottom which, with the addition of plating on top, gave a firm foundation for the machinery. More strength was given by dividing the hull with traverse and longitudinal watertight walls or bulkheads. Six masts were fitted, with rigging of wire rather than of hemp. (This was not a success, though she possessed excellent sailing qualities.)

The engines [Plate 19] consisted of four fixed cylinders, in fact a 'double triangle-frame engine'.[1] In the middle of the overhead crankshaft, between the two sets of triangle-frame engine big-ends, was an 18¼-foot drum. Over the blocks on this drum ran four chains which engaged with blocks on a smaller drum below, between the two triangle-frame engines, which drove the propeller shaft. Thus the engine speed of 18 revolutions per minute was geared up to a propeller-shaft speed of 53 r.p.m.; Brunel would have none of the crude gearing which marred the *Archimedes'* performance. The shaft itself was hollow throughout most of its length. It drove a six-bladed propeller, each blade composed of a tip or palm riveted on to the end of an arm.

Accommodation was provided for 252 passengers and 130 crew, with 1,200 tons of cargo and 1,200 tons of coal. With such luxurious accommodation, and fares between £20 and £35, the ship was built like the GWR for those who wanted the best, and not for a mass market. The first plate was laid on 19 July 1839, so she was well under way in the company's own dry dock

1. The triangle-frame engine was shaped like an inverted 'V' with the crankshaft at the apex, and the cylinders at the lower extremities. Patented in 1822 by Marc Brunel, it was used on top of the Rotherhithe shaft of the Thames tunnel where an engine which worked with less than usual vibration was required, and developed in marine use into the 'inclined' or 'diagonal' type which powered most pleasure paddle-steamers.

1. Isambard Brunel aged 23: a portrait by his wife's brother,
J. C. Horsley. *(British Railways Board)*

2. Sir Marc Brunel. This portrait, completed when he was over seventy, shows the Thames Tunnel in the background. *(National Portrait Gallery)*

3. Isambard Brunel's bold design for the Clifton Bridge, showing the roadway springing directly from the face of the gorge. *(Author's Collection)*

4. The Clifton Bridge in Victorian times, his profession's monument to Brunel.

12. The up station at Reading in 1899, looking towards London from the roof of the down station. By this time the main changes are the construction of a wooden platform joining the two stations, and the removal of broad-gauge rails. Top: Plan of the station *c.* 1850. *(British Railway Board)*

13. One of the famous broad-gauge 4-2-2s, Daniel Gooch's masterpiece, when new, on the Bristol and Exeter Railway. The 'policeman' in uniform, just visible at the far left, was the forerunner of today's signalman.

17. The s.s. *Great Western* in an Atlantic gale. The virtues of great longitudinal strength in such conditions are obvious.

18. The s.s. *Great Britain* being fitted out at Bristol in 1845. This photograph, perhaps the first of any steamship, shows clearly how the lines at the stern followed sailing-ship practice. *(National Maritime Museum)*

19. Model of the engines of the s.s. *Great Britain*. The shaft to the propeller is at the bottom of the engine. *(Science Museum)*

20. A composite portrait of those concerned with the Britannia Tubular Bridge over the Menai Straits. Robert Stephenson is seated in the centre, with Captain Claxton (bespectacled) behind him. Brunel is seated at the extreme right. *(British Railways Board)*

21. Model dwellings for artisans. Commissioned by the Prince Consort, shown at the Great Exhibition of 1851, and commended by Brunel's Committee. A view of them as re-erected on Kennington Common, London.

at Bristol when they decided on the screw propeller. Hence the importance of Brunel's point that changing to the screw could be done without expensive changes in the hull design.

After the departure of Humphreys, the whole supervision devolved upon Brunel, Guppy, and Claxton. Slow progress was made – there were money troubles as usual – but four years to the day after she had been started, she was floated out into the Floating Harbour. Prince Albert graciously presided, amid excited throngs of bonnetted and umbrellaed Bristolians. The rain wasn't allowed to spoil things, and there was a good lunch. Afterwards the GWR – D. Gooch presiding – whirled the royal visitor away Londonwards, and the fitting of the engines began.

Getting the ship out into the open sea was another matter, and when they tried on 10 December 1844, she almost stuck in the lock leading from the Cumberland Basin into the river. Claxton – nautically in charge as usual – and Brunel just saved her from being stuck fast by the falling tide. Some heavy work on the masonry of the dock enabled them to get out on the next tide, in the dark. So the *Great Britain* started life with a narrow escape. In the New Year she steamed round to London to be visited by the young Queen and her consort. It was a very rough trip which she used to demonstrate her superiority over any other ship afloat. Their Majesties were followed by 1,500 less exalted Londoners daily till June, and then by 2,500 Liverpudlians daily. On 26 July 1845 she left Liverpool for New York, by which time she had cost over £117,000.

Why Liverpool? The simple answer is that she was too big for Bristol. Despite Brunel's earlier reports and work, the harbour there continued to silt up, and the dock company were not willing to improve the locks. They were, however, only too willing to impose heavy port dues on the two great ships of the Great Western Steam-Ship Company, and this drove them away to Liverpool, the hated, successful, rival port where the dues were one-half those of Bristol.

The voyage to New York took just under fifteen days, and in truth the new ship was little faster than the *Great Western*. Considerable vibration was experienced, and that she shed parts of her propeller in the next few voyages is not surprising in the light of subsequent propeller development. In the winter of 1845 the propeller was replaced with a four-bladed one. With the loss of a mast and some re-rigging, her sailing qualities were improved against the necessity of repeating Capt. Hosken's feat of bringing her home under sail in eighteen days on the second round trip, after she had lost most of the propeller. In 1846, performance improved and business began to look good.

At midday on 22 September 1846 she left Liverpool on her fifth voyage. With a south-easterly wind, Capt. Hosken elected to go south of the Isle of Man, then pass between it and Ireland, round the north of Ulster, and so into the open sea for New York. He would meet fewer eastbound ships that way than if he went south of Ireland, and in those days of oil lights, that would be all to the good, for the weather was thickening up and it was going to be a nasty night.

About 5.30 p.m., logging about eleven knots on an approximately north-westerly course, they saw the south end of the Isle of Man, but the weather then closed in. About 7.00 p.m., Hosken remarked to his First and Second Officers that 'they must be well up by now with the Calf', one of the small islands at the southern end of the Isle of Man. He gave orders to shorten sail and come round to a course just east of north, about 8.00 p.m. This was being done when a light, soon observed to be revolving and flashing, was seen on the port bow. Thinking it was the Calf of Man, they came back to a north-westerly course and Hosken, perplexed, asked: 'How is it possible she has not run her distance; what can have held her back?' There should have been two lights if it *was* the Calf of Man, but the thickening weather could well be preventing a sight of the second one. By the time they got this flashing light on the correct bearing for a safe passage round the southern tip of the Isle of Man, it was 9.15 p.m., and they came to northward. When Hosken realized the time he ran down to check the chart, because they should have been well clear of the island long before. He emerged to shouts of 'shoal water!'. His immediate reaction was 'hard-a-port, stop her', but at the same moment she ran aground where there should have been deep water. Where were they?

Hosken had not been a sea-captain since the 1830s without having a cool head. He had the engines put astern and backed the yards to try to get her off, but they were aground on a falling tide and it was no use. The only thing to do was to sit it out till daybreak should reveal where they were. He calmed the passengers, though few got much sleep. When the dawn broke, they found that they had run aground on the Irish coast. As the *Liverpool Mercury* said later: 'She went too quick to turn the corner and ran her head, as it were, against the opposite wall. Barring Ireland in the way – and Ireland is always in everybody's way – the navigation would have been perfect.' The light they had taken for the Calf of Man, to be passed on the starboard hand, was one on the Irish coast which should have been left to port. The light they could still see was on St. John's Point, but it was not on Hosken's chart. His conduct after they struck redeemed him, and in the morning the locals did a roaring trade in rescuing passengers and baggage from the ship.

The ship was now Hosken's real worry. So far she seemed to be in one piece though she had been banging up and down all night in an ominous way, despite the ostensibly sandy bottom. In the next few days they tried all sorts of shifts to get her off, but the weather kept ships at a distance, and towing was unsuccessful because she was on a dead lee shore for the southerly gales. To try to preserve her from the worst of them Claxton, who had hurried over as soon as he could, set sails and drove her further up the beach. Brunel was heavily engaged with railway affairs in Devon and Westminster, and he could not visit the scene until December. She was then still hard and fast aground in Dundrum Bay, and Isambard let rip at Claxton in a letter which tells us a lot about a man whose masterpiece has been nearly ruined by irresolution, poor planning, and a lack of concerted action.

The stern of the ship was still very much at the mercy of the sea, and protecting it was a far more urgent and vital task than devising means of getting her off, but no protection had been arranged. 'The finest ship in the world . . . has been left like a useless saucepan kicking about on the most exposed shore that you can imagine, with no more skill or effort applied to protect the property than the said saucepan would have received on the beach at Brighton.' But then, so typically, he goes on to outline a plan for 'poulticing' the exposed part of the ship with a mass of faggots of wood lashed together, to break the force of the sea. After a lot of trouble, Claxton and Hosken managed it, and the next step was to lighten her by taking out coal and other moveables. By various means, the ship was raised so that some of the holes could be patched, and by August 1847 she was buoyant enough for the high tides to float her off, still leaking but afloat.

They kept her afloat by furious pumping until she was towed over to Liverpool where she could be repaired.

The whole sorry affair *could* have been a much greater disaster, but happily no lives were lost. Because the *Great Britain* was only insured to the extent of a £17,000 mortgage on her, in effect her owners had to bear the whole cost themselves, and the company was liquidated. On the credit side, it is probable that no other ship in the world could have survived such a battering as she took between September and the time the protective poultice was completed, so the ship's great strength from Brunel's hull design was completely vindicated.

Characteristically, despite some pretty hard letters to Claxton himself about what he was not doing, Brunel's reports to the directors always contain a reference to Claxton's zeal, energy, persistence, and skill. Claxton's heart was in the right place and, as Brunel well knew, all he needed was sound and energetic leadership, with an occasional touch of the spur. They were a great partnership, and great friends. One of Isambard Kingdom Brunel's most attractive traits was that he lost few opportunities in his reports of mentioning in the most favourable terms some good work done by a worthy assistant. Although he longed to distinguish himself in the eyes of the world, he never tried to keep all the credit to himself: he seemed positively to delight in being able to share it with a subordinate whose work had pleased him.

The rest of the *Great Britain* story cannot be told, because it is not finished yet. After passing through various hands, and being re-engined and re-rigged, she was finally converted to a sailing ship in 1882. On her third voyage round Cape Horn she was badly damaged by weather and put back to the Falkland Islands. From 1886 to 1937 she was used there as a hulk for storing wool and coal, and was finally scuttled at Sparrow Cove in 1937, aground for the second time. And for the second time she has been rescued. To those who knew she still survived in the far-off Falklands, and dreamed wistfully of visiting her, the successful salvage operations of 1970 and her return to the dock of her birth in Bristol seems like a miracle. Let this chapter end with the words of Brunel's first biographer, his son: 'She remains to testify to the ability and wisdom of those who were daring enough to build so large a ship of iron, and to fit her with the screw propeller.'

8   The Spread of the Broad Gauge

Brunel's life is remarkable for many things, and not the least of them is the way in which he carried on a number of great enterprises simultaneously. They were often enterprises which involved changes in the established order of things and were thereby of considerable consequence. His reports on specific projects often give the impression of a man doing three things at once. He is bringing forward the practical results of scientific experiment often at the frontier of scientific knowledge. At the same time he is analysing and conquering the practical problems of detail, because he was never satisfied with something that would work on paper but might not on wheels. And all the time he is considering and suggesting how the work to be done should be managed and supervised, always trying to forestall possible trouble. It is often said of him that he had a gift for picking subordinates and collaborators to carry out his plans, but this underrates his gift for managing affairs as well as men. These gifts, plus boundless energy and enthusiasm, explain how he was able to carry on so many projects simultaneously.

His interest in the shipping revolution did not cause him to abandon railway work. The extension of the railway from Bristol to Exeter was started before the GWR main line was complete, and the nationwide railway activity which brought the GWR and London–Lancashire routes into existence also turned attention towards the area of country between them. Besides the Bristol & Exeter line, therefore, plans were already afoot in 1835 for a Cheltenham & Great Western Union line, to join the GWR at Swindon.

The Cheltenham & Great Western Union Railway would also reach Gloucester, and at this point there appeared one of the great trunk routes which would not touch London. The railway developments in Lancashire and North-east England had been quickly taken up in the Midlands, and by the late 1830's there was active support for a line south from Birmingham towards Bristol. In the Cheltenham area, the Birmingham &

Gloucester, and Cheltenham & Great Western Union Railways agreed to have a form of joint ownership. Southwards to Bristol the ground lay with the Bristol & Gloucester Railway which had grown out of the old Coal Pit Heath Tramway. The problem which arose after these lines were opened in the early 1840's was that from Birmingham to Gloucester the lines were of the 'narrow' gauge (4 ft. 8½ in.) but from there to Bristol they were of the GWR broad gauge (7 ft.). In 1844 Gloucester was the first point where the 'break of gauge' occurred, and it rapidly became a place of notorious difficulties.

In spite of many suggestions, some of them even practical, for dealing conveniently with traffic passing at Gloucester from one gauge to the other, the original method of handling the traffic continued: passengers changed carriages, and goods had to be unloaded and reloaded. Delays were continual, as were losses and damage. Understandably the advocates of the narrow or standard gauge made a lot of these troubles, which broad-gauge supporters tended to blame on a lack of accommodation 'and more or less intentional mismanagement'. This referred to the fact that the Gloucester arrangements were under the control of the (narrow gauge) Birmingham & Gloucester Railway, and even after the creation by amalgamation of a Bristol & Birmingham Railway the problem continued. It was made worse when in 1845 the Midland Railway leased this amalgamated concern, even while the GWR were still haggling over the terms for buying it.

It would be outside the scope of this book to go into details of the building of all of the lines which figured in the 'Gauge War'. In any event, Brunel's connexion with them was far less intimate than with his original main line. They do, however, contain a few notable examples of his work, such as the original bridge across the Wye at Chepstow.

In the 'Gauge War', the arguments of 1838 were brought before a wider audience. There was some preliminary skirmishing with the London & South Western Railway, in the area which had formed the possible southern route for the GWR main line, though peace had been restored by 1845. But north of the main line, battle was joined.

The westward extensions of the broad gauge in the country north of Bristol did not of course stop at the River Severn. From the early days of the GWR, as we have seen, Brunel was influenced by the need to have access to the prosperous districts north of the main line, which the Cheltenham & Great Western Union Railway now tapped. He was also looking to South Wales, although the east-west trunk route there did not come about until after the events of the 'Gauge War'.

By 1844 the broad gauge had reached north to Oxford, and the next objective was Rugby on the London & Birmingham Railway, for Rugby was then the key to the East Midlands and the North. The GWR was interested not only in the Oxford and Rugby line, but also in a line to the heart of the narrow-gauge territory – the Oxford, Worcester & Wolverhampton Railway, whose subsequent rake's progress earned it the nickname of the 'Old Worse and Worse'. To add to the confusion at this time when the railway mania was beginning to gather momentum, there was also a Birmingham & Oxford Junction Railway. This was promoted by the Grand Junction Railway (Liverpool/ Manchester–Birmingham) to give them access to London independently of the London & Birmingham Railway.

At that time the government concerned itself very little with the promotion and building of railways, in contrast to the situation on the Continent. The flood of railway schemes in 1844, however, caused Parliament to take a hand by the appointment of five Commissioners of the Board of Trade, the department responsible for all railway matters, to act as a court of preliminary hearing. To a legislature faced with a surfeit of schemes which it would never have time to investigate fully, this Commission was a useful expedient; to railway promoters locked in combat with their rivals, appearance before it was regarded merely as the first round in the contest.

The battles for the right to build lines from Oxford to Rugby, Birmingham, and Wolverhampton and north towards the Mersey, raged for several years. The struggle for control of the lines north of Wolverhampton went on until 1854; in Dorset and Devon there were equally protracted squabbles, but the details of these affairs need not concern us. Although arguments about the gauges were often used, the real fight was commercial, for possession of the territory through which the line passed, and for the traffic and profits it could bring.

In all this, Brunel was from time to time called on to play a part, sometimes as an engineer, once as the 'general' of an army of navvies, more often as a witness before parliamentary committees. Apart from the details of the lines under consideration, he was closely questioned about the merits of his broad gauge, his most singular contribution to the development of railways to date, and what effects it would have on the growth of rail communications. As we have seen, Brunel's gauge was not without opponents from the very beginning. A new one was Richard Cobden, the apostle of Free Trade and a stern opponent of customs barriers between nations. Perhaps he saw the break of gauge as a similar barrier to the growth and spread of prosperity within Britain. After unsuccessfully leading the parliamentary opposition to the broad gauge for the Oxford, Worcester, & Wolverhampton Railway, Cobden induced the House of Commons to set up a Royal Commission on the subject of railway gauges, and this started to hear evidence in 1845.

Brunel's reasons for proposing the broad gauge have already been examined. As far back as 1837 Joseph Pease M.P., son of the Stockton & Darlington Railway pioneer, had moved a notice of motion in the House of Commons to fix the gauge of all railways to one standard. Urging Lord Grenville Somerset to oppose it, Brunel wrote:

'We maintain that 7 feet is a very great improvement as regards economy of transport, speed, and safety, and moreover that the uniformity of width in all railways is not in practice of any real importance, and consequently to limit our gauge to that hitherto adopted is to stop improvement, to the serious injury of the public and of the Companies, and that the only result would be to benefit existing railways by thus preventing improvement in others.'

In the public battle of the gauges, as distinct from the struggles for commercial supremacy by gaining control of various railways, there were two main areas of conflict. One was the dispute as to which of the gauges was actually better; the other was the problem of their incompatibility. Those supporting the broad gauge pointed to its manifest superiority in terms of speed, and the convenience of its carriages, although they were badly shaken in 1845 when the Commissioners pointed out quite fairly that 'the actual speed of trains upon the GWR is not so high as upon some narrow gauge railways.' In May 1845, express trains from London to Exeter were notably speeded up in consequence, to 43·1 m.p.h. including stops.

In the same report it was alleged that broad-gauge railways

cost more to make and more to run, but Brunel was always emphatic in denying this. He argued that the increased width of earthworks and structures was trifling in proportion to the total width, and that vehicles also cost little extra, due only to the greater length of axles and cross-members. In addition, he pointed out that the higher working expenses on the broad gauge were not in the main due to the gauge at all, but to the higher overall standards maintained on his railway. The truth probably lay somewhere between the two. Brunel was constantly insistent on the fact that the public wanted faster and more comfortable trains, in which the broad gauge then excelled; he argued that they would continue to demand improvements, and, most important, that only the broad gauge had the potential for improvement.

To demonstrate this he proposed that the Commissioners should hold a series of competitive trials, to examine the relative performance of broad-gauge and narrow-gauge engines. Trains of several different weights were to be run, over varying distances. This sporting challenge was taken up in a rather half-hearted way by the narrow-gauge party, and trials of a much less ambitious nature were eventually held, between Paddington and Didcot, and between York and Darlington. The attempts by the narrow-gauge party to rig the trials in their favour merely had the effect of reducing the disparity between the performance of the two contenders. On its best run the GWR train of sixty tons ran most of the way at 55–60 m.p.h., with a fastest mile of 62 m.p.h. The best the narrow-gauge could manage, with fifty tons, was to run most of the way at about 50 m.p.h., with a 54 m.p.h. maximum. The rigging of the York and Darlington trials prevented an accurate comparison of fuel consumption. The trials confirmed what experienced travellers already knew: the broad-gauge at that date was better.

Brunel stressed that not only was it better then, but that its superiority would increase because the narrow-gauge was at the limit of its development. Although they incorporated all the latest design improvements, the poor performance of the narrow-gauge engines supported Brunel's view. The intended improvements in design of these narrow-gauge engines in fact made them less safe, and the trials were concluded when one of them damaged the track so badly that it was derailed. Yet within a few years the narrow-gauge was running trains as good as those of the broad.

There was an inconsistency in Brunel's arguments. As his 1837 letter reveals, he was resisting compulsory uniformity because it would remove competition between various systems, which was bringing continuous improvements. He maintained this position before the Gauge Commission:

'I believe', he said, 'that a great deal of the progress that has been made in railways has arisen from the fair emulation that exists between the promoters of the two gauges . . . and that the system of generalizing, whether the gauge or anything else, would do more harm than good.'

Few people would disagree with his proposition that improvements came from competition; yet he ignored the conclusion that competition would lead to improvements in the narrow-gauge as well. His view seems to be based on the point that the distance between the rails would limit the size of narrow-gauge engines and rolling-stock, and that it would for ever remain trapped at that limited stage of its development. Of course it did not, because the overall maximum size of vehicles – the loading gauge rather than the rail gauge – is the more effective limitation. Developments in the twentieth century with steam on gauges of much less than 4ft. 8½in. have produced train performances unimaginable in 1845. But nobody pointed out Brunel's inconsistency at the time.

The other main area of the arguments was the problem of incompatibility between the two gauges. It had arisen at Gloucester in 1844, and the northward extensions from Oxford were certain to make it more and more a matter of contention. So far Brunel's arguments concentrated on superiority and the possibility of improvement, so he strongly resisted compulsory uniformity on those grounds. Against him were the difficulties that the break of gauge was already causing, and would increasingly cause, as the points of contact multiplied. How did he deal with this attack?

Firstly, he argued that the points at which the break of gauge occurred were often those where an area of the country devoted principally to one kind of activity, like manufacturing, adjoined another area devoted in the main to another activity like farming. The breaks of gauge would tend to be at the 'natural frontiers', in a geographic and economic sense. In 1845, with its northern boundaries at Oxford and Cheltenham, this was true of the

GWR. The argument would support broad-gauge extensions to Rugby, and as far as, but not through, the Midlands. So far as passenger traffic was concerned, he took this point further. He argued that cost would prevent any widespread use of through carriages, except along main routes like those to and from London. Passengers on most other routes would therefore have to change carriages anyway, and so a break of gauge at such a place would not add further inconvenience. Specifically he did not forsee any significant through passenger traffic over the route through Rugby–Oxford–Southampton, or across London.

Turning to goods traffic, he again made his point about the virtues of competition and went on: 'As regards goods it is of course a mere question of money. Some inconvenience will occur. The amount of it will depend very much upon the particular line of country, and upon the interest of the parties on either side, either to increase or diminish the amount of that inconvenience.' He was ready with a solution, in case the will 'to diminish the amount of that inconvenience' was lacking, as it certainly was.

For through bulk traffic like coal, they could use a transferable wagon-body – today called a container – which could travel on either a narrow-gauge or a broad-gauge chassis, and be transferred by crane. Such containers were already in use for the Bristol & Exeter Railway's seaborne coal traffic. Using containers for the through traffic would mean, if the narrow-gauge parties co-operated, the building of specialized rolling-stock. Brunel argued that their self-interest would urge them to this. The expansion of railways was causing much new stock to be built, and the need to provide special vehicles for the break of gauge problem would be embraced within the general need to provide more of every kind. If they were blind to their own self-interest, and would not co-operate, the energetic architect of the broad-gauge had an answer ready. It was a broad-gauge transporter truck, which would have narrow-gauge rails on to which a narrow-gauge wagon could be run.

One such transporter was actually made, and the Commissioners were offered a view of it. Sending broad-gauge trucks over the narrow-gauge in a similar way (though this time, of course, using a narrow-gauge truck with broad-gauge rails on it) would of course be more difficult, but, as the operators envisaged more traffic coming from narrow-gauge to broad than *vice versa* and consequently a continual surplus of narrow-gauge wagons going home empty, the problem was a small one.

Brunel seems to have sensed that, logical though his arguments were, men – even those 'commercial men' whose virtues and influence were so highly regarded in Victorian England – did not always see or follow their own self-interest. He therefore proposed that in the Wolverhampton–Worcester area there should be a three-rail mixed gauge system to facilitate heavy short-distance traffic in the south-west Midlands.

He did not always have a smooth passage, for, on occasion, he had recommended the narrow-gauge for railways in Wales and in Italy, where he had designed a line from Florence to Pistoia. His answer was simply that in those cases the speeds and loads required of those railways would not require the power obtainable only on the broad-gauge. They might therefore improve their positions by having the same gauge as their neighbours.

Many other witnesses were heard; the Commissioners deliberated; and then they came down against the broad-gauge. Some of their conclusions were questionable, and the GWR party attacked them hotly. However, at the centre of their report, while acknowledging the present superiority of the broad-gauge for express trains and the few who used them, the Commissioners saw that as of far less moment than the general convenience of the country; that general convenience would be best served by a uniformity of gauge, and that the degree of convenience so obtained would outweigh any slight inferiority of the narrow-gauge for some purposes. On the possibility of improving the narrow-gauge performance they were silent, but recommended that the conversion of the broad-gauge to the narrow should be done at the public expense.

The GWR party reacted vigorously, but the Commissioners seem to have realized that the superiority of the broad-gauge benefited only a small part of their traffic, and was concerned mainly with speed. The difference in speed between the two was not enough to offset the time lost because of the break of gauge. The expense of this operation, plus the loss and damage, decisively tipped the balance in favour of uniformity. Without saying so, they seem to have appreciated the inconsistency in Brunel's argument about the relative development potentials of the two systems.

The result of all this effort was the Gauge Act of 1846 which at first sight confined the broad-gauge to the GWR and the counties south of it. Section 2 of the Act, however, threw the whole question wide open again by excepting any new railway if its enabling act contained a specific clause as to its gauge. As MacDermott says: 'Thus did the Broad Gauge party succeed in spiking the great gun of the enemy, to the intense annoyance of the latter.'

The fact remains that the subject had enjoyed so thorough an airing that the balance of informed opinion was ever after against the broad-gauge, on the ground of the overwhelming benefits of uniformity. It also remains to be recorded that the Board of Trade ordered the laying of narrow-gauge rails on the vital Oxford & Rugby Railway. This led rapidly to a link-up of narrow-gauge rails along the Rugby–Southampton route, joining up the northern and southern rivals of the GWR. It was the first nail in the coffin but, like Charles II, the broad-gauge was 'an unconscionable time a-dying', and by the time the last line was converted to narrow-gauge in 1892 it had outlasted both Brunel and Gooch.

Any modern assessment of the question, and Brunel's part in it, must be tainted with wisdom of hindsight. The explosion of economic and social activity which called for railways nation-wide would favour uniformity, especially as the subsequent history of the narrow-gauge was much more successful than had been predicted. Rather, alas, it was the broad-gauge which, ever more isolated, made little further progress after the 1850s. Although the GWR got all the way to the Mersey at Birkenhead, it did so on narrow-gauge rails. The broad-gauge reached only to Wolverhampton, and the GWR in the Midlands was mixed gauge from the start. This allowed a growth of traffic which saved the fortunes of the company in the lean years of the great agricultural depression from 1873–1896, which was severe in the southern and western counties.

Looking back to the arguments of 1845, we can see that Brunel's great competitive principle did not promote the better and extinguish the inferior. Rather the reverse, for it was a stimulus to the narrow-gauge, which had the advantage of being in possession of the major areas of economic growth: the coal-fields and the industrial districts. Where there was a major traffic flow through a break-of-gauge point – such as the Midlands to the south-west, or Rugby to Southampton – the self-interest of the parties led either to a parallel narrow-gauge route, or to the mixing of the gauges and through working; never to containers and transporter trucks.

How much of this did Brunel forsee? He lived less than ten years after the end of the Gauge War, more and more divorced from railways affairs, which became increasingly distasteful to him. 'I prefer engineering very much to projecting of which I keep as clear as I can,' he said. He never gave up his gauge, but he must have realized that its adoption or rejection was no longer decided on its merits, but as a tactic in railway politics. It seems unlikely that he could not see that the commercial impetus behind the narrow-gauge system would in the end establish it everywhere, perhaps to the extinction of his system. He did not live to see the narrow-gauge improvement challenge the broad-gauge. Perhaps, then, although he guessed what might happen, he preferred to withdraw from what was essentially a commercial struggle into the always more satisfying task of solving engineering problems. Both on land and sea, his greatest tests were still to come.

> *Gone is the Broad Gauge of our youth,*
> *Its splendid course is run.*
> *It has fought the battle nobly*
> *But the Narrow Gauge has won.*
> *Alas for good Sir Daniel,*
> *Alas for bold Brunel,*
> *They are resting from their labours,*
> *They are sleeping: it is well.*
>
> *Anon.*

In pleasant contrast to the gloom surrounding the demise of the broad-gauge we can return to the days when it was new, when it bestrode the West Country like a colossus. The Bristol & Exeter Railway (B&ER) was promoted in Bristol in 1835, and perhaps because the potential traffic did not seem very great or very lucrative it was sanctioned without major opposition and had no competitors. The survey was done by one of the assistants from Brunel's Thames Tunnel days, William Gravatt, who had been a pupil at Bryan Donkin's engineering works, during the short time Isambard had also been there. The B&ER was leased by the GWR before opening, and when completed to Exeter in 1844 it was found to have been built within the original estimate of two million pounds, which was unusual in those days. There were also sundry branches, but it did not contain any features of special note. In the Gauge War the company was, of course, an ally of the GWR.

The parliamentary success of the B&ER was followed by proposals for a railway on from Exeter to Plymouth in 1836, but money was short and they came to nothing until 1843 when the GWR and B&ER companies put finance and life into them.

In building the South Devon Railway, Brunel had to contend with a number of problems familiar to all railway engineers, but in a particularly acute form. The country to be crossed between Exeter and Plymouth included several of the southern spurs of Dartmoor, with deep river valleys between them, which meant that the gradients would be heavy, but not impossible, for by the 1840s the ability of the locomotive to climb gradients was improving rapidly. The second problem was the sparsity of potential traffic and no prospect of large profits, with a consequent restriction on capital for construction. For both these reasons, it was vitally important to build and work the line as cheaply as possible.

Brunel always stoutly opposed the idea that a broad-gauge railway would cost a lot more than one with a narrow gauge, and

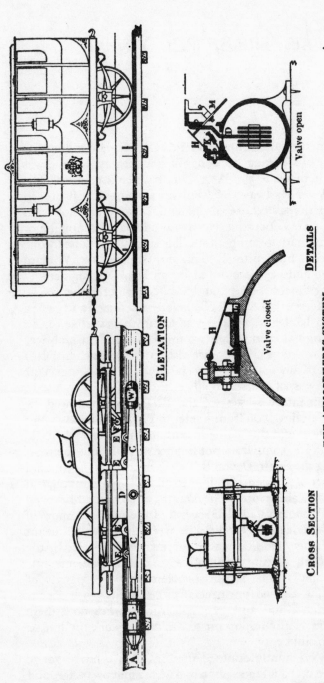

ELEVATION

CROSS SECTION

DETAILS

Valve closed

Valve open

THE ATMOSPHERIC SYSTEM

A.A. Continuous Pipe fixed between the rails.
B. Piston.
C.C. Iron Plates connected to the piston.
D. Plate connecting Apparatus to Carriage.

E. Metal Rollers to open the Continuous Valve.
F. Roller attached to Carriage for closing the Valve.
H. Weather Valve.[1]

K. Continuous Airtight Valve hinged at l.
L. Composition for sealing Valve.
M. Roller attached to Carriage for opening Weather Valve.[1]
w. Counterweight to Piston.

[1] These complications do not appear to have been in use on the South Devon Railway.

in any event an attempt to economize by using the narrow gauge would have serious effects on the profitability, because the South Devon was part of a through route to the west. Traffic in Devon was not expected to be enough to need a double track; and a single line could deal with the number of trains required. Brunel at that time had some doubts about ensuring safety on a locomotive worked single-track railway in the absence of a means of communicating instantaneously between the two ends of the section, and there was to hand another form of propulsion which might be used with less hazard in these circumstances. This system would have a higher capital cost, but against this could be put the savings of building only a single line. The system would also allow steeper gradients and sharper curves, both of which would help to reduce building costs.

He proposed to adopt what was called the 'atmospheric system', which for a brief while greatly appealed to railway engineers. It was one of those mechanical marvels which appear from time to time, and look too good to be true. Brunel – ever searching for the better way – was quite taken up with it, and in this he was not alone, for M. Mellet, reporting to the French Minister of Public Works, wrote: 'its use will do away with the useless weight of the locomotive or, where stationary engines are used, with that of cables.'

Between the rails was a cast iron tube, fifteen inches in diameter, with a slit in the top, which was normally closed by a continuous leather flap fixed to the tube along one of its edges. The other edge was not fixed but free to lift if pushed up from within the tube by a roller, falling back again by its own weight and that of the iron plate along the top of the free edge after the roller had passed [see previous page]. Where this free edge of the leather flap or valve rested on the tube, it bedded into a composition of tallow, oil, soap or beeswax, making an airtight seal. The tubes were in ten-foot lengths, socketed together, and connected at intervals to stationary steam-engines, driving vacuum-pumps which exhausted the air out of the tube.

The trains were hauled, not by a locomotive, but by a piston-carriage. Inside the tube was a round-headed piston covered with leather, on the leading end of an iron plate fifteen feet long, which had a counterweight on its other end. At intervals on the top of this plate, and running inside the tube, were roller wheels which pushed the leather flap up, temporarily breaking the airtight seal as the piston went along the tube. Through this temporary opening passed the bar (called a 'coulter') connecting the piston-assembly to the piston-carriage above it, and behind the coulter there was another roller hanging down beneath this carriage which pressed the leather valve shut again. The piston moved forward by virtue of the atmospheric pressure behind it in contrast to the 'partial vacuum' in front of it, which the stationary engines created, and as the piston moved, so did the piston-carriage and the train. There were many complications, but the patentees, Clegg and Samunda, were gradually overcoming them.

The atmospheric system had originated around 1810, and Brunel had done some experiments with it in 1840 on a section of the temporarily cash-starved West London Railway, close by the GWR at Wormwood Scrubs. Next came the opening in Ireland in 1844 of a 1¾-mile extension to Dalkey of the pioneer Dublin & Kingstown Railway, working on the atmospheric system. It worked quite well, too, especially as there were many sceptics who said it would never work at all. The Irish company was using it because it offered the prospect of economies in both construction and use. The first came from the reduced costs of earthworks consequent upon its hill-climbing ability and the sharper curvature possible with safety due to the stabilizing effect of the piston; the second came, as the French engineer had said, from doing away with the useless weight of the locomotive. It was cheapness in these respects, rather than mere mechanical novelty, which made Brunel decide to recommend the system in South Devon, where capital was in short supply, but where there was no shortage of gradients and curves.

Nor was there any shortage of critics of the atmospheric system, and a clash of the giants took place before the parliamentary committee on the Croydon & Epsom Railway, which was going to use it in continuation of the section from Forest Hill to (West) Croydon. Leading the opposition was Robert Stephenson who, like Brunel, had looked into the merits of the system but had come to the opposite conclusion. The two engineers tacitly agreed that the system was not yet perfect although it might be made so, but Stephenson doubted whether the forecast economies of construction and working could be realized. The nub of these economies was that a single atmospheric line could carry the traffic of a double line worked by locomotives. Stephenson's main objection was that there would be considerable difficulties in operating the traffic of such a line with regularity acceptable to the public, and, therefore, in order to achieve satisfactory working, they would be driven to build a double line thus losing much of the saving in construction cost. As we shall see, in Brunel's own estimates for the SDR, the saving due to the single line was by far the greater part of the whole. Stephenson also said that his experiments cast doubt on the economies in transmitting power by what he called a 'rope of air', from the stationary engines to the piston-carriages. Although Parliament sanctioned the Croydon & Epsom Railway, there was a further confrontation in 1845 before a Select Committee of the House of Commons. But before this, in August 1844, Brunel had taken the momentous step of recommending the atmospheric system for the South Devon Railway.

In his report to the directors, Brunel openly made two assumptions: first, that because the cost of moving the locomotive would be avoided, stationary power would be cheaper and better if the rope could be dispensed with, and second, that 'as a means of applying stationary power the Atmospheric System has been successful and . . . it is a good economical mode of applying stationary power.' He goes on:

I am aware that this opinion is directly opposed to that of Mr. Robert Stephenson, who has written and published an elaborate statement of experiments and calculations founded upon them, the results of which support his opinion.

It does not seem to me that we can obtain the minute data required for the mathematical investigation of such a question, and that such calculations, dependent as they are upon an unattained precision in experiments, are as likely to lead you very far from the truth as not.

By the same mode M. Mellet and other French engineers have proved the success of the system; and by the same mode of investigation Dr. Lardner arrived at all those results regarding steam navigation and the speed to be attained on railways, which have since proved so erroneous.

In other words, the arithmetic is not soundly-based enough to decide the question, but the Dalkey line is doing well. Brunel, however, did not attempt to demolish Stephenson's other main criticism (besides the one that the great economies from atmospheric working had yet to be realized on a line of any length) that operationally the chain of pumping-stations was like any other chain, only as strong as its weakest link. The sole working atmospheric line was only $1\frac{3}{4}$ miles long, with only one pumping-station, and it remained to be proved that the system could work with decent regularity over a much longer distance, let alone with a mixture of passenger and freight traffic, for the Dalkey carried only passengers. The South Devon was going to provide that proof, and cost less to build than a locomotive line in the process.

At first sight, the reduced capital cost is the major reason for abandoning locomotive haulage, but, as the total saving was to be only about £60,000 on a capital of £1,100,000 for fifty-two miles of line, we might reasonably ask if this really was Brunel's principal reason for this momentous step. After all, it represents a mere five per cent of the total capital cost, and, although the B&ER had been built within the estimated cost, Brunel was as well aware as any engineer that such an event was exceptional. Because over-expenditure was far more common, most estimators, then as now, added ten per cent to cover unexpected expenses, so that in theory the capital saved by having the new system could be lost again in these unforeseen expenses. What other reasons were there, and what can we guess about the order in which Brunel would put them?

He advances an expected saving of £8,000 yearly on working expenses which represents less than a one per cent dividend, and he also forecast that, because the power plant was already there, the increased cost of working extra trains as traffic required would, compared with locomotive haulage, be very small. Then there appears a most significant sentence.

It appears to me also that the quality of the travelling will be much improved; that we shall attain greater speed, less noise and motion, and an absence of the coke dust which is certainly still a great nuisance.

These advantages he reckoned would also increase the journeying of those who travel solely for pleasure, or at least not out of necessity, and such people he thought to be the majority of travellers. In an area which was only then beginning to be a place for holidays, this seems very doubtful.

Brunel had quite enough past experience to know just how reliable construction estimates were, and his own arithmetic must have shown him that the reduced working cost would not enable a golden harvest of dividends to be gathered, even on the hopefully reduced capital. Just how much extra traffic the advantages of the system would generate must also have been uncertain, given the fairly sparse population of the district. It looks as though Brunel's optimistic nature wanted to believe that these economies could be realized, and he used them to reinforce his other reasons to himself and his directors. He wanted to give a real trial to a system that might revolutionize railways, and would also improve the quality of travelling, which he rightly believed the public would always support.

This report is dated 19 August 1844, and the directors soon made arrangements with the patentees to use their system, tenders being invited for the tube and the stationary engines. There were some delays in constructing the line – the sea-wall section along the seashore between Teignmouth and Dawlish gave some trouble – but by May 1846 the line from Exeter to Teignmouth was ready. The atmospheric system, alas, was not. The tubes, however, were laid and valved by the autumn, but locomotive haulage continued because of unexpected difficulties with the least novel part of the system, the stationary engines. Although ordered from the most reputable firms, Maudslays amongst them, the engines were not well made, and cast iron was used where wrought iron would have been wiser, so that it was February 1847 before the first trial of a piston-carriage could be made. Another seven months elapsed before the public service began, but little by little the atmospheric system took over and by January 1848 virtually the whole daytime service over twenty miles from Exeter to Newton Abbot was run without loco-motives. Ominously, the atmospheric working of the Forest Hill–Croydon part of the London & Croydon Railway had been abandoned in May 1847, when the extension to Epsom was opened. The tube had been too small, and this caused a shortage of power which could be overcome only by uneconomical working. This disastrous pattern was soon to be repeated in Devon.

The South Devon was virtually a sea-level line from Exeter to Newton Abbot, and the first stretch of heavy gradients lay beyond, crossing the watershed between the rivers Teign and Dart. As atmospheric working began to settle down to a routine on the section to Newton Abbot, there was great interest in how it would cope with the 1 in 45 gradients up to the watershed summit at Dainton; but they never found out. Although the train service appears to have been as regular as it ever was with locomotives in the 1840's, the leather valve began to decay for various reasons. There had been trouble during a frosty winter, but in the dry May and June of 1848 long sections of the valve had to be replaced because it was torn. Although under their contract with Samuda the cost of replacement could be set against his patent fees, the effect of the damage to the valve was more far-reaching. It caused train-working delays, of course, but much more serious was the leakage of air into the tube. The stationary engines had to be worked faster than their designed speed, which caused expensive breakages in that department and had the overall effect of pushing up coal consumption. This was made worse because the tube was of too small a diameter and therefore needed a greater and more leak-prone level of vacuum to move the trains, and the pumps were too small to achieve this without overdriving the engines. Delay in extending the electric telegraph into the stationary engine-houses also increased their difficulties, because it meant that the engines were started according to the time-tables, regardless of the fact that the train for which a vacuum was being created might well be late, either because of the heavy gradients to the west (the line was open to the outskirts of Plymouth by May 1848) or because of working delays on the Bristol & Exeter line to the east. The cumulative effect of the leakage, the undersized vacuum-pumps, and bad communications, was soaring expense for coal, and the italianate chimneys of the engine-houses belched forth smoke into the Devon air to the annoyance of the residents, as the enginemen thrashed their inefficient charges to produce the vacuum required.

By June 1848 it became apparent that the only way the system could be kept going – let alone keep its costs to something near the forecast level – was by a complete renewal of the valve at a cost of £25,000. There was also the disquieting fact that the twenty miles of atmospheric apparatus had cost, not £95,000 as Brunel had estimated in 1844, but well over £400,000. The tube had cost at least twice as much as estimated – in part this must have been due to scrapping three miles of 13-inch tube ordered for the flat portion of the line. It is almost impossible to explain the gross over-expenditure in detail, but the inescapable facts facing the South Devon board were that something like £425,000 had been spent on the atmospheric system so far; that another £25,000 was the minimum that would keep it usable over the first twenty miles of their line; that equipping the further thirty miles to Plymouth would cost a great deal more than Brunel's estimate; and, finally, that it was by no means certain that still more money would not be needed before the system could have a chance of even equalling the working costs of locomotive power. Forced to face these facts, Brunel put them squarely to his board. On the experience of working to Newton Abbot he could not recommend extending the system to Totnes and beyond, and, unless Samuda was prepared to renew the valve and keep it in repair, they would not be justified in spending money on bringing the stationary engines up to scratch on the section already working. Presented with Brunel's report, the board did not hesitate; the locomotives took over on 6 September 1848.

So the atmospheric system became one of mechanical history's might-have-beens. The reasons for its failure compounded one another, but even if it had worked with the promised economy, free from expensive technical imperfections, hindsight makes one aware of the enormous difficulties in operating a railway with the normal fluctuating traffics of different sorts. More important for us, is to try to see clearly what was Brunel's part in this financial débâcle. Some conjectures as to his motives for starting the project on the South Devon line have been put forward already, and it cannot be denied that during the winter of 1846 and spring of 1847, when the atmospheric equipment was being installed, Brunel must have been preoccupied with the troubles of the *Great Britain,* ashore in Dundrum Bay. But apart from some bad design and workmanship on the stationary engines by firms of repute, who should have known better even though they were very busy, the troubles of the system were inherent within it, and in the way in which it was applied on the SDR.

The main trouble which magnified problems with the leather valve, was that neither the tube nor the engines which exhausted it were properly proportioned for the work they had to do. The tube was too small for the weights of train to be moved, so it needed a higher degree of vacuum which increased the risk of leakage. The air-pumps were too small so that the steam-engines connected to them had to be driven faster than their designed speed, causing breakages and excessive coal consumption. Brunel's responsibility in all this must be shared with Samuda, for they underestimated the size of tube required, as well as mistaking the proportions of the engines and vacuum-pumps. Samuda's responsibility is, however, much less than Brunel's when we consider how grossly the estimates were exceeded. The atmospheric system failed because it cost too much to run, as well as imposing an impossible capital burden on its owners by costing too much to build, and, as both these major errors were fairly and squarely Brunel's province, he must bear the major responsibility for the failure. The £350,000 dead loss almost bankrupted the SDR and, as the B&ER had provided £200,000 of capital and the GWR £150,000, the experiment was costly to both these companies too.

Westwards from Plymouth lies the Duchy of Cornwall, and the promotion of the South Devon Railway to Plymouth inspired the idea of carrying it through to Penzance. In that early industrial area around Hayle and Redruth, local enterprise had created what was basically a mineral railway in 1834, but it was not until the period of railway mania in 1845 that things really began to move, only to come to a halt again when the mania collapsed in 1846. During the period the atmospheric system had come into prominence, and, despite the misgivings of the B&ER and GWR who were putting up nearly £200,000 of the Cornwall Railway's capital, the provisional board decided to use it. With the chronic shortage of capital after 1846, no further progress was made, perhaps happily, in view of what was going on between Exeter and Newton Abbot. Another event was the decision to cross the Tamar river valley by a high-level bridge at Saltash rather than by a steam ferry. The successful building of this structure is a happy counterpoint to the débâcle of the atmospheric system, although it was to put a great capital burden on the sparse traffic of the Cornwall Railway, covering the sixty miles from Plymouth to Falmouth. Pointing out that the aftermath of the railway mania had left many contractors looking for work, and that railways would never be built so cheaply again, Brunel had tried to awaken the sleeping Cornwall company in 1850. He wrote: 'I have been daily expecting to hear something from you about the Cornwall. Is anything doing, or are we taking another nap?'

However, by 1853 having decided to build only a single line and practising strict economy, they were able to begin work on fifty of those miles, including the bridge. In the event the cost of the bridge extinguished the independence of the railway, because, as it was built, the company had repeated recourse to the railways to the eastward for guarantees of its shares; but as the Cornwall formed part of the broad-gauge route to the west, there was no damaging conflict of interest.

The Tamar at Saltash is 1,100 feet wide and about seventy feet deep at high tide. The land on either side slopes sharply down to the water, and, as the Admiralty required a clear head-way under the bridge of 100 feet at high water, it was clear that the piers of the bridge would have to be very high. Trial borings revealed about seventeen feet of mud on the bed of the river, and solid rock below that. Brunel's first decision, therefore, was how many piers to construct, because he had to strike a balance between the cost of piers and the cost of longer bridge spans. Eventually he decided on a bridge with a number of simple approach spans, and two principal spans of 455 feet resting intermediately on one deep water central pier. The building of this to above the high-water mark occupied the years 1853 to 1856, and although virtually none of it is apparent to an observer, in fact it represents the most difficult part of the whole job.

Brunel's first problem was to explore the underwater rock, and this was done in 1848. He drew on his Thames Tunnel experience in using the diving-bell, and a trial cylinder, six feet in diameter, was sunk into the mud of the river bed, then pumped out so that it settled, allowing them to excavate down to the rock. When money again became available in 1853, an iron cylinder, ninety-five feet in length, long enough to go right down through the water and the mud to the rock, was made, incorporating some suggestions from Brunel's assistants, Glennie and Brereton. A section of it appears at the right of plate 26 which, with the following description, is taken from the 1870 biography.

The cylinder had a diameter of 35 feet at the bottom, and about 20 feet above the lower end of it a dome was made to form the roof of the diving-bell. From the centre of the dome rose a tube 10 feet in diameter to the level of the top of the great cylinder. As a diving-bell of this size under 80 feet of water, might have proved unmanageable, an annular space, forming a galley or jacket 4 feet wide and 20 feet high, was formed round the inner circumference of the bottom of the cylinder below the dome. This annular space (divided by radial vertical partitions into eleven compartments) was connected at the top by an air-passage with a 6-foot cylinder, which was placed eccentrically inside the 10-foot cylinder already mentioned, and served as a communication between the outside and the annular space. On top of the 6-foot cylinder were placed the air-locks of the pneumatic apparatus which had been used at Chepstow [in sinking the river piers for the South Wales Railway bridge there]. Thus air might be pumped into the annular space, the water expelled, and the work carried on without having to use air pressure under the whole of the dome.

By sealing the outside of the annular space, and pumping the mud and water out of it, they were able to cut away the rock under the mud and build a ring of masonry on to it. This sealed off from the river the inner space under the dome which was likewise cleared and filled with masonry, after which the plates between the two spaces were cut away and the outer ring of masonry joined up with the central portion built under the dome. Thus they effectively sealed the bottom of the cylinder, and the rest of the pier was built up inside it, the ironwork within being removed as they built upwards. When the pier was completed to above the high-water mark, the upper part of the great cylinder which was in two parts was unbolted and taken ashore. Brunel's proper sense of economy defeats those who might look for relics of it, because it was cut up and used for decking the pontoons on which the bridge trusses were floated. Similarly the 6-foot trial boring cylinder of 1848 was used for one of the internal cylinders in 1853.

On the Devon shore, the great trusses of the bridge were being built, and these must now be described. For many years Brunel had made occasional experiments to examine the strength of various shapes of iron girder by testing them to destruction, and thus he had evolved his favourite girder which had a round or oval tube for its top flange. In the Saltash bridge each truss is composed of one of these oval tubes, arched, with its ends resting on the central pier and on one of the land piers. Below each tubular arch, and 'mirroring' it, is a pair of suspension-bridge chains, hanging from either side of the tube. The force they exert to pull the pier down inwards is balanced by the tube above, its arched form holding the piers apart. The deck of the bridge (on which the rails were laid) is hung from both the tube and the suspension-chains. Sadly, some of these chains had been made for the Clifton bridge, still uncompleted for want of money [Plate 25].

The operation of floating these trusses, each weighing over 1000 tons, and raising them into position on top of the piers, had in a sense been pioneered by Robert Stephenson in building the Britannia Tubular Bridge across the Menai Straits, and Brunel had readily responded to Stephenson's invitation to be present to assist, with Capt. Claxton in charge of the nautical arrangements. At the Tamar, docks were dug in the shore under the ends of each truss, and pontoons were floated into them at low water. The pontoons rose with the tide and thus each truss was lifted, being then drawn out into the stream by hawsers from the hulks in the river until the ends of the trusses were floating just above the top of the centre pier and one landward pier respectively. When the tide fell again it left the truss sitting on the top of three hydraulic presses, any two of which could if necessary lift the end of the truss, and, as this was done, the piers were slowly built up under the presses, until the truss was 100 feet above the water. The great cylinder was positioned in May 1854, and by November 1856 the central pier was ready. The first truss was floated into place on 1 September 1857 and by the following May it was at its full height. The second truss was floated in July and reached its full height by December 1858.

Brunel personally supervised the operation, assisted by Captains Claxton and Harrison, and his chief assistant, R. P. Brereton. To avoid confusion and mishap it was necessary that only one person should control the movement and that everyone else should take their orders directly from him, so that, although an immense audience assembled on both sides of the river, the job was done in total silence, broken only by cheering when the job was done and the truss in position. By 1858, however, Brunel's health was failing, and his last adventure was claiming all his ebbing strength. But he did see the finished bridge, from a couch on a specially-prepared wagon, drawn slowly across by an engine in 1859, after the Prince Consort had ceremonially opened it and named it the Royal Albert Bridge. Despite some latter-day alarms, the bridge stands today carrying trains far heavier than those of its youth. In part it owes its longevity to being made of wrought iron which resists corrosion so well. With a restraint which its architect would have approved, the only ornament is the inscription placed by the railway company above the arches of the landward piers, through which the trains pass under the great tubes. The inscription reads simply:

I. K. BRUNEL

ENGINEER

1859

Brunel's other West Country monuments have not survived so well. It will be remembered that among the obstacles facing the South Devon Railway was the number of steep-sided river valleys running down to the sea, each presenting a gradient problem, and often a bridging problem as well. This pattern was repeated in Cornwall, as was the shortage of capital, and in consequence there arose the famous timber viaducts, of such fragile appearance that at first the locals were afraid to trust themselves to them, but which stood without failure for many years. Basically they were of two types, depending on the depth of the valley and the foundations available. Where the valley was very deep, but with a dry bottom, masonry piers were built up to within about thirty-five feet of the bridge decking. Where the valley floor was tidal, the whole structure was timber right to ground level, resting on pile foundations driven into the mud. All of these viaducts – and there were sixty-three of them in Devon and Cornwall, between twenty-five and 150 feet in height and up to a quarter of a mile long – were replaced by 1934, but they were a feature of the western landscape in their time. As far back as 1841 Brunel had built two timber bridges on the original GWR main line, and, by making strength experiments with timber in the same way as with iron, he was able to perfect a design which was strong yet economical, and quite the reverse of the trestle log matchwork, once so characteristic of North America.

The secret, as in so much of Brunel's work, was in the perfect adaptation of form to function. The loads on each timber were calculated, and the eye can see exactly how the design worked, with all the simplicity of a diagram. As well as *looking* right, they *were* right, and they never failed even though some of them were built on reverse curves, and even though the Cornwall Railway staged a head-on collision on the one at St. Germans. The weights of the trains increased, the viaducts had to be strengthened, and the timbers slowly decayed; but by standardizing his designs Brunel made it possible for defective members to be replaced piecemeal without disturbing the structure or causing more than a very short suspension of traffic. In the end, it was the rocketing cost of the proper timber which forced their replacement. It is regrettable that not one survives, because the design was as carefully worked out as the great Saltash Bridge, and they were probably the last, and, some say, the finest, major works of timber bridge-building in England.

10 A Question of Mathematics

Today, when any new works are required by British Rail, the design and planning of them is the task of a staff of civil engineers who are employed by the railway. But the railways which Brunel built were virtually all planned and designed by him and his personal staff of clerks, draughtsmen and assistants. Most of this work was done at the house into which he had moved shortly before his marriage in 1836 at 18 Duke Street, Westminster, which was later extended to include No. 17. Here, for over twenty years, Brunel's faithful clerk, Joseph Bennett, served his master and his wide-ranging concerns, the sober copperplate with which he copied the letters into the letter-books getting steadily less legible. Brunel himself wrote a spiky Victorian scribble, obviously in a great hurry most of the time, and researchers who use the letter-books sigh with relief as they come to the mid-1850's when the staff was obviously augmented by a new clerk with a most legible style who took over some of the humbler duties like the letter-book, though 'J. Bennett' still did his share. Indeed, as his master's fatal illness progressed, all the letters are from him on behalf of Brunel, including that sombre document in which he first writes of 'the late Mr. Brunel'.

The Brunel family lived 'over the shop' as it were, but, in accordance with the literary conventions in 1870, when his eldest son wrote the first biography of Isambard Kingdom Brunel virtually the only reference to the family is 'He married the eldest daughter of the late William Horsley, and granddaughter of Doctor Callcott. Of this marriage there was issue two sons and a daughter, all of whom survive him.' The biography was written by Isambard III, who was born in 1838, followed by Henry Marc and Florence. Isambard III became a lawyer specializing in ecclesiastical matters, and Chancellor of the Diocese of Ely; Florence married a master at Eton; Henry Marc alone followed his father's profession of engineering, though not to such eminence.

Their father's activities from the later 1830s enabled the family to live in style in Duke Street. Although Brunel often thought it right to back schemes in which he was engaged, by taking up shares in them and sharing the risks with the promoters, it is an open question how much money he made in doing so; certainly financial pressure in 1838 compelled him to sell a portion of his GWR shares. Although he made and spent a great deal of it, money was certainly not the mainspring for his great achievements. (His correspondence shows that in 1836 he charged seven guineas a day plus expenses for the services of himself and his personal staff, and that this had risen to ten guineas by 1844.) In addition to these sums, there would be professional fees from various sources, although there were often delays of several years before these were received. By 1850 his income was running at £15,000 to £20,000 a year, an immense sum for a professional man in those days, and it probably exceeded even that range in the 1850s. He took pupils into his office ('I do take pupils – or rather I have been driven to take them', he wrote) but he made the point that they would receive no formal instruction, being taught nothing beyond what they could pick up for themselves in a busy office – and the premium for these pupils was deliberately pitched as high as £1000 for a three-year period, to keep the numbers down.

Furnishing and embellishing the house in Duke Street took quite a lot of this considerable income, and one part of the house in which Brunel undoubtedly found great joy was in the nursery upstairs. Like his father before him, who gave ha'pence to the clean children of Rotherhithe and the same to the dirty ones if they would go away and wash, he delighted in the company of children. Many Victorian parents of the upper classes found that the early years of their children's lives were an inconvenience, so the children grew up in the company of maids, nurses, and governesses, very much out of contact with their parents. To the young Brunels with their father so often away in the country on business or attending at Parliament till all hours, his appearance was a cause for rejoicing, because, once freed from the cares of business, his love of fun and imaginative invention readily turned towards all sorts of wonderful delights for them.

On 3 April, 1843 during one of these romps in the nursery he was doing some of the conjuring tricks with which *his* father used to amuse his children. In pretending to pass a half-sovereign from his ear to his mouth, the coin he placed in his mouth slipped down his windpipe and lodged at the bottom of the right bronchus where it joins the lung. The only immediate ill effects were a slight discomfort and repeated coughing, so nothing was done for a fortnight and then Sir Benjamin Brodie, probably the most notable surgeon of his day, was consulted. By getting his distinguished patient to lean over a chair, Sir Benjamin discovered that the coin was loose – indeed Isambard felt it move – but it would not come out. Brunel then had a device made for tipping himself upside down, but when it was first tried he coughed until he nearly choked. Brodie next tried to remove the coin by using the forceps which bear his name, an especially long pair designed to be passed down the windpipe, but these also nearly choked his patient. Recourse was therefore had to surgery in an attempt to make another less dangerous entry for the forceps. This also failed and, somewhat at a loss as to what to do next, they reverted to the 'Brunel Inverter', and this time it worked. With great relief Brodie seized the coin as it fell, and after forty days and nights of danger Isambard was able to breath freely again, and to write that evening to Claxton, busy with the *Great Britain* in Bristol: 'At 4½, I was safely and comfortably delivered of my little coin; with hardly an effort it dropped out, as many another has, and I hope will, drop out of my fingers. I am perfectly well.' The accident was so extraordinary, and Brunel by then such an eminent figure in London that when Macaulay, the historian, ran through the streets to the Athenaeum and shouted, 'It's out', everybody knew what he meant. *The Times* noticed his recovery, and also published a long letter explaining how the coin had been recovered. Brunel was lucky to get away with his life, and not for the first time. The episode figured in one of the *Ingoldsby Legends,* as part of the *Moral* to 'The House Warming':

> Young Gentlemen, too, may I think take a hint,
>   Of the same kind, from what I've here ventured to print.
> All conjuring's bad! They may get in a scrape
>   Before they're aware, and, whatever its shape,
> They may find it no easy affair to escape.
>   It's not everybody that comes off so well
> From legerdemain tricks as Mr. Brunel.

Life at Duke Street resumed its normal course, with Isambard away very frequently, and extremely busy when he was at home. His wife, Mary, devoted herself to the social round, with separate carriages for mornings and afternoons, and a grand air of state about her. One wonders what old Sir Marc and his Sophie thought of it all, when they came to stay, for it was not till 1849 when he was eighty-one, that Isambard's father died. And the former Miss Kingdom, now Lady Brunel, so far from the terrible convent at Gravelines, lived on with her son and his family until January 1855. One wonders too what the older generations thought of the state of things in 1848, the Year of Revolutions, when Isambard enrolled as a special constable for Westminster. He had taken no active interest in politics since the election of Ben Hawes in 1832, but in 1848, out of curiosity, Brunel and his brother-in-law, John Horsley, went to revolutionary Paris, armed with introductions as 'Citoyens Horsley and Brunel'. This was one of a number of continental excursions Brunel made with Horsley – an extended one, partly on Italian railway business, took them to Rome where the exterior of St. Peter's was considered a disappointment – but Mary did not like travel and generally remained in London with the children, to whom she was obviously devoted. But lest it be thought that all was either domesticity or engineering at Duke Street, it should be recorded that among the callers were many of the foremost artists of the time (in the mainstream of the visual arts at any rate); and they participated in the decoration of the dining-room, which Brunel grandly named the 'Shakespeare Room', because it was hung with scenes from the plays.

His London house was rented, but in 1847 Brunel bought some land at Watcombe, near Torquay in Devonshire. At that time he was very busy with railway-building in the West Country, but his plans for Watcombe indicated that he had it in mind as a more permanent base. To say that he was tiring of his profession in 1847 would ignore that some of his greatest triumphs were yet to come, but undoubtedly there were factors which induced him, as he put it, 'to draw in and make room for others'. His style of life since 1834 had been one hectic rush, and from time to time his health gave warnings that this could not go on for ever. In the late 1840s also, the development of railways in England had changed from being bold, inventive pioneering and had become much more a matter of money and speculation, which Brunel found distasteful, and which he saw would lead to a bad crash one day. Using some of his ample fortune to provide a place of relaxation in one of the most beautiful parts of Devon therefore made excellent sense, but only the garden was completed, and the house which he planned was never built. From the house that never was, however, we can turn to some completed buildings in which he did have an active part.

If we leave aside the humble buildings for domestic, farming, and other uses, most buildings until the end of the eighteenth century were planned by an architect, or a master-builder working very closely with his client, who also supervised its construction. But the separation of civil from military engineering gave rise to a new breed of men who created large buildings which were not used for domestic, military, or religious purposes. For instance, many architects were involved in providing large buildings for the railway companies, and working alongside them were the new civil engineers, whose skill and activities extended beyond buildings to include many other things, including earthworks, tunnels, bridges, and docks; and both civil engineers and architects worked on a new type of building especially evolved for railways – the train-shed – and we have already noticed Brunel's early work on it at Bristol.

Creating the railway from Bristol to London meant that Brunel was, as engineer, concerned with many other things beyond the normal run of an architect's work, but this did not mean that he was not concerned with the appearance of the structures. Promoters and engineers alike were usually concerned that their railway should not be without ornament in the appropriate places. A study of the portals of tunnels between London and Bristol, particularly of their original appearance, shows Brunel to have been a master of many of the styles of architecture which could be applied ornamentally, and he did not keep to any one type. However, on the GWR as elsewhere, when railways increased and became much more the subject for commercial speculation, less and less attention was paid to architecture. Individual companies evolved their own standard version of a utilitarian style, and there was less money for ornamentation or individuality. On the Great Western group of lines, this probably meant that Brunel was often concerned only with the style of the most important buildings, in contrast to the early days when he designed virtually everything himself. However, at the beginning of the 1850s he was required to produce a major work, for, with the opening of through lines to Birmingham and South Wales, the GWR had outgrown its original London terminus.

When the first Paddington station was built, Bishops Road bridge formed its front, giving an approach from the street which was far from grand and not at all in keeping with its position as the citadel of the Broad Gauge. The goods station was built to the east of it on the south side, on the site originally intended for the passenger station, but in the 1850 scheme the new passenger station was to take over its rightful position, and a design in keeping with its importance was required. By that time it was foreseen that the volume of traffic would grow to require a station with more accommodation than just one arrival and one departure platform with carriage sidings in between, and the new station had a double-sided intermediate platform between those alongside the walls. It was also still considered the best plan to have the whole area under cover, and the methods of achieving this all-over roofing had advanced considerably since the late 1830s. The great discovery was the way in which cast iron and glass could be united to cover a large area quite cheaply without either the massive foundations or the complications that earlier buildings enclosing a large space had required. It was the availability of iron as a material for structural members carrying balanced loads, allied to mass-produced glass, which brought about this change, which was pioneered by the Palm Stove of 1844–7 at Kew, mainly the work of Richard Turner (though commonly attributed to Decimus Burton), and more spectacularly by Paxton's 'Crystal Palace' for the Great Exhibition of 1851, where he developed the original ideas he had used in the conservatory at Chatsworth (1837).

Brunel sent a competition form and a circular letter to thirty-three of his assistants in which 'Mr Brunel calls your attention to the enclosed, and hopes you will try and send some good design.' His own part in the Great Exhibition did not lead to any work of consequence, although he was a member of the committee which rejected all the designs preceding Paxton's, and had its own design rejected by the public. That had incorporated a high dome which was Brunel's idea, though of the permanent brick buildings proposed he 'thought them misplaced, as others do the dome which I defend as a striking feature to exemplify the present state of the science of construction in this country.'

Paxton's design, however, was in fact far more to Brunel's liking;
he supported it, and happily it was the one which was built.
When a new station was needed at Paddington, therefore, the
new 'railway-shed style', as Brunel called it, was an obvious
choice. To buildings using all kinds of materials ornamentation
had been added, and when the new manner of using cast and
wrought iron made its appearance, it too was ornamented.
Brunel considered this outside his scope, and he called in the
assistance of Matthew Digby Wyatt who was also much occupied
with the Great Exhibition. Wyatt was then principally known,
not as an architect, but as something of an authority on decorative
features in buildings, and his work on the new station was entirely
complementary to that of Brunel, who concerned himself with
'the department which I keep to myself, namely the general
design'. Brunel admitted that 'for detail of ornamentation I
neither have time or knowledge', but this was Wyatt's speciality,
and in 1852 he published a book on metalwork and its artistic
design. Wyatt's work at Paddington has been praised, pilloried,
and even parodied, and an attempt to appraise it here would be
contentious. It is not style or lack of it on Wyatt's part which is
significant, but rather that Brunel thought it worthwhile to care
about the details when he could so easily have opted for a simple
engineering solution to the problem of roofing the train-shed.
He was not only concerned with engineering and ornament, but
also with colour: 'I want to show the public also that *colours* ought
to be used.' His career had come a long way from the pleasing
watercolour sketches of his various Clifton Bridge designs, but to
Brunel colour still mattered. As John Horsley said in 1870: 'So
small an incident as the choice of colour in the original carriages
of the GWR, and any decorative work called for on the line, gave
public evidence of his taste in colour; but those who remember
the gradual arrangement and fitting-up of his house in Duke
Street will want no assurance of [his] rare artistic feeling.'

Brunel's feeling at this time, as an artist as well as an engineer,
was that a station should be no mere shed, nor yet an imitation of
some building in one of the classic styles of architecture which had
themselves evolved for a particular purpose. Instead he was one
of the first to see that a station had special problems, and that the
solving of them with the methods and materials newly at hand
was the right thing to do. It would be an exaggeration to say that
he and those who took a similar view founded another style of

architecture to rival the Grecian or the Byzantine, but they did succeed in achieving their purpose in an efficient, harmonious, and even graceful way. Ironwork building continued, and during the nineteenth century it gave birth to some fantastic confections in the course of concealing by ornament and otherwise the nature of the material used. Only in the steel-framed glass-walled buildings of our century have we again come to terms with the materials in a way pioneered by Paxton, Brunel, and others.

Happily, Brunel's Paddington is still with us, with more platforms but still serving its purpose of keeping the weather out. Unfortunately his work in connexion with the Crystal Palace, after it had been moved to Sydenham at the close of the exhibition, does not remain. He was represented there by two giant water towers, one at each end of the building, but these were demolished in the present century after the Crystal Palace itself was destroyed by fire in 1936.

The happy memories of the Great Exhibition of the Works of Industry of All Nations were supplanted in the minds of the British public by the outbreak in 1854 of the Crimean War. During the first winter of hostilities the shortcomings of the War Office and the command in the field became apparent, as stories of an almost total lack of proper equipment and stores began to come back to England. When further news of the appalling overcrowding and disastrous conditions at the principal military hospital at Scutari also became known, the government fell, and a mild sense of urgency began to pervade official circles in London. Among them was Sir Benjamin Hawes, Brunel's brother-in-law whose first election in 1832 seemed now so long ago. Hawes had become Permanent Under-secretary at the War Office in 1852, and in February 1855 he approached Brunel with the request to design a hospital which could be made in England and sent out in parts to the Crimea. The staff at Duke Street were obviously driven hard, for in only three weeks a complete design was ready, and in less than a month from the original request one of the wards was erected on GWR land at Paddington. This enabled the details both of construction and the medical arrangements to be examined and amended before mass production started. Brunel, characteristically, had on his own initiative ordered the manufacture of some of the components of a 1,000-bed hospital, but his forceful nature, and perhaps his close friendship with Hawes, overrode the timorous departmental protests at such an outrage.

By May the first parts of the hospital were on the site. Although it was intended to use supervised local labour at Renkioi, in fact none worth having was available, so the eighteen English craftsmen and two engineers had to do it all themselves. By July the hospital was ready to receive patients, though none were sent till October 1855, when it could have taken in nearly 1,000. The speed of design, manufacture, and construction which this time-table reveals is remarkable in itself, but the hospital at Renkioi is deserving of our notice for other reasons too; reasons which tell us a lot about the way Brunel attacked a problem.

The hospital was a series of wooden buildings, each a 50-bed ward, on both sides of a central open-sided corridor, and at right angles to it. Thus the layout of the buildings was a first line of defence against airborne infection spreading from ward to ward. In his directions to the men he sent out to build the hospital, Brunel insisted on the fundamental importance of method in doing their work, and doing it in the right order. Thus, the water-supplies and the drains must come first, instead of a rush to put up the prefabricated wooden wards. Once these essential services had been provided, wards could be erected as and when the need for them arose. Similarly, each of the ships carried a certain number of complete buildings 'so that by no accident, mistake, or confusion, short of the loss of several of the ships, can there fail to be a certain amount of hospital accommodation, provided with every comfort and essential.' This was the same methodical approach which had been used in circumstances such as floating the trusses at Saltash, and it, rather than brilliant improvisation, was the hallmark of Brunel.

A second significant thing about Renkioi hospital is the way cleanliness was achieved, not by draconian orders about procedure in the wards, but more effectively by designing the place so that hygienic conditions were created, or at least assisted, by the plan adopted. The sewers, for example, ran outside the two rows of wards, and not under the central corridor which would perhaps have been the obvious choice, though not the most sanitary. Similarly there was an emphasis on ventilation. 'If I have a monomania it is a belief in the efficiency of sweet air for invalids', said Brunel, and this caused him to provide each ward with a ventilating trunk under the floor between each of the two double rows of beds. There was even a hand-driven fan at the corridor end of each trunk to force air through, but, as the hospital was built on a windy ridge, the fans were never needed. Indeed there was such emphasis on ventilation that one wonders if the patients did not sometimes long for a somewhat less breezy situation. In that respect Brunel's design was very much of its time, equating evil smells with the carrying of infection. And as an indication of just how backward the common soldier was known to be in matters of basic hygiene, not only were water closets and lavatory paper provided, but also handbills, telling the men how to use them, and exhorting them to do so.

The emphasis on method, cleanliness and sanitation achieved its object, for out of a total of 1,400 patients only about fifty died, and one of the remarkable things about the whole adventure was that the cost of the complete 1,000-bed hospital, such a great improvement on Scutari, was only £22,000. The pity of it all was that Renkioi came too late, for it took in patients for only five months, and was never even half-full. By May 1856 the war was over, and the hospital was empty again, being dismantled to be sent back to England or sold on the spot. Brunel's contacts with government departments had rarely been happy because he was one of the 'new men' of business, very different from the officials who had grown old in the service and set in their ways. Probably in this instance it was the collaboration with Ben Hawes, and his power over the administrative machine, which for once enabled Brunel to carry out his plans in detail and without delay, in a public department. Florence Nightingale thought that Hawes was the biggest villain of the whole sorry Crimean affair, but whatever the truth is, a lot of men owed their lives to the Renkioi Hospital.

11 'Great Eastern'

Besides bringing Brunel directly to the aid of his country, the Crimean War also indirectly affected him, because the *Great Britain* played a part in the war. Although she had been sold because of the winding-up of the Great Western Steam-Ship Co., following the near disaster at Dundrum Bay, she had not been broken up, but was being used by Gibbs, Bright & Co. of Liverpool on the Australia run. In 1854, on completing her third return voyage, she was chartered by the Government as a troop transport to the Crimea, although she did not carry any parts of Renkioi hospital during her ten months' service. While she had been earning profits for her new owners on the Australian run – the gold rush was at its height – Brunel had been thinking about another ship which would be as much an advance on the *Great Britain*, as that vessel had been on the *Great Western*.

As far back as 1851 shipping interests had been thinking about the possibility of going all the way to the Antipodes by steam, but the problem was as usual coal capacity. Consulted by some interested parties, Brunel had recommended what was, in effect, the *Great Britain* solution all over again: a bigger ship which would not need the same increase in power in proportion to the increase in its size, so having a greater proportion of its capacity available for passengers and cargo. At that time he recommended a ship of about 6,000 tons which would need to take on coal only at the Cape on the outward run; returning via Cape Horn, she could be coaled in the Falkland Islands. The *Victoria* and the *Adelaide* were built in consequence, although Brunel had no hand in them.

Apart from Australasia and India, British involvement in the Far East generally had been growing rapidly in the first half of the nineteenth century, with the establishment of trading footholds at Singapore (1819) and Hong Kong (1842). Our interests in the East in that period were mainly commercial, and a rapid expansion of trade in both directions took place. From Australia came wool for the growing West Riding industry, and gold from the finds of 1851. For the outward journey there was a growing emigrant trade (transportation to Australia as a punishment for crime ceased in 1840), as well as cargoes of manufactured goods of all kinds. Various companies were formed to establish shipping lines from Britain to places in the east, but in March 1852 the Peninsular & Oriental Co. secured the government contract to carry the mails, removing at a stroke the secure financial basis for developing an eventually profitable business so far as other companies were concerned. Among them was the Eastern Steam Navigation Co. of 1851.

In June 1852 Brunel approached the directors of that company, who were then somewhat at a loss to know how to keep their organisation alive, with a project for building a ship big enough to go all the way to Australia without recoaling. He wrote:

The same amount of capital and the same expenditure in money for fuel now required for a line of ships of the present dimensions, would build and work ships to carry in the year double the number of passengers, with far superior accommodation, and in about half the time, and about two or three times the amount of cargo; the whole difference being produced simply by making the vessel *large enough to carry its own coal*, exactly as when the *Great Western* was projected for the New York line, the passage had been considered an impossible one for steamboats, or, if possible, only at a total sacrifice of all return for the cost.

What he had done with the *Great Western* and the *Great Britain*, he could do again, and, such was his reputation, that, notwithstanding the initial lack of financial success on the part of the *Great Britain*, which was in fact just starting to make good profits for its new owners, his plan was adopted for two ships each of about 21,000 tons displacement.

These ships would be big enough to get to Calcutta and back without recoaling, but, as the depth of water in the Hooghly at Calcutta would limit the amount of cargo with which they could return, it was thought probable that they would recoal at Trincomalee so as to be able to leave Calcutta with as big a cargo as possible. Equally, they could get to Australia and back without recoaling, but this would not leave much room on the outward trip for cargo in addition to about 3,000 passengers, although about 3,000 tons of cargo could be brought home. If, however, coal was loaded in Australia, then 3,000 tons of cargo could be carried in *each* direction. Whatever the details of coaling arrangements, the great delays of recoaling at intermediate ports on the voyage out and on the voyage home would be avoided, and there would be real savings in time. Even the 3,000-ton *Great Britain* took eight days to recoal at Cape Town on an Australian voyage of eighty-six days, of which only seventy-two were actually spent at sea; bigger ships could make more round voyages in a year by avoiding these delays.

Having accepted Brunel's ideas for these gigantic ships, the directors' next step was to raise the capital, for it was estimated that each ship would cost half a million pounds. Raising the money took a year, and Brunel had to use his personal influence, and his own money, before the company was ready to let contracts for construction. This fact, more than any other, tied him psychologically to the enterprise, because he felt that many of those who had put their money into it had done so on his recommendation, and it explains in part why his interest in the project became an obsession.

He considered various sets of dimensions for the ships, and eventually settled on a length of 680 feet, an 83-foot beam, and a 25-foot draught. There were to be two independent sets of engines, one to work the screw propeller, and the other to work the 60-foot paddle-wheels. With these dimensions, tenders were invited for the first ship, and eventually that for the hull was awarded to John Scott Russell of Millwall on the Isle of Dogs, in the Thames. Russell also contracted to build the great oscillating engines for the paddles. The engines for the screw were contracted for by James Watt & Co., the total contract sum of the hull and engines being £377,000.

Details of the hull design set a pattern which has lasted until today. The ship was to have two skins, one inside the other, with about 3 feet between the plates, so that she would not flood even if the outer skin was holed. Within the inner hull she was to be divided by ten watertight transverse bulkheads going up to upper-deck level, and two additional longitudinal bulkheads were to be provided in the centre section to sub-divide the large boiler and engine compartments. In a report, Brunel expressed his view that even if the ship should break in two each part would float independently. In the event of both skins being holed, at least one and probably two complete sections between bulkheads could be flooded completely without causing the ship to founder. He did not use the word unsinkable, but that was the impression given.

So gigantic an undertaking, so many years ahead of contemporary designs, gave rise to many problems of detail as well as of arrangement of the principal parts, but we have space to notice only a few. For instance, because ships were often forced into port to repair defects associated with bilge-pumps, Brunel permitted no openings of any sort, even for pipes, in the ship's bottom, nor was even the inner skin penetrated below the loaded water-line, so that many defects which would ordinarily mean a diversion to a port, could be repaired at sea. Another notable feature was obviously born out of the *Great Britain* disaster which occurred primarily because those in command were not sure precisely where the ship was. Brunel proposed an observatory, continuously manned by trained staff, 'the primary object being to be *constantly* determining either correctly or approximately the ship's true position, and in a like manner *constantly* checking the compasses and giving her a true course.' The observatory would contain not only a full-time staff constantly ascertaining the ship's position, but also an embryonic gyro-compass, and a sea-water fountain, the temperature of which could be taken regularly in cold latitudes, to give warning of icebergs. Finally, to revert to basics, the ship would have those hallmarks of a Brunel design: a concentration of longitudinal strength, and a meticulous disposition of material so that every piece of iron carried a load. None of the iron was to be there to make 'convenient the mere *putting together* of the whole as a great box'. She would be a bigger and better 'floating structure' than the *Great Britain*.

Work started in the spring of 1854, when the first plates were laid. As yet no name had been decided upon. The ship was built parallel to the river because her great length not only made it impossible to launch her across the river without very great danger, but also to avoid the difficulty, in giving the necessary inclination to the launching ways, of having the forecastle 100 feet off the ground. Limitations on expense precluded the building of a large enough dock for 'floating out' in the fashion of the *Great Britain*. Scott Russell's own shipyard was not nearly big enough, so most of the ship was built on Napier's empty yard next door, rented for the purpose – Napier had moved to the

Clyde precisely because the growing size of ships made the Thames less and less suitable as a place for launching. The paddle-engines were built alongside in Russell's workshops, and Watts built the screw's engines at the famous Soho Foundry in Birmingham. Scott Russell had the modern notion of providing a huge crane which would have been able to reach over quite a lot of the site, but this was not allowed on the score of expense, so each of the 30,000 wrought iron plates, 10ft. by 2ft. 9in., had to be hauled aloft with hand-tackle [Plate 30].

Scott Russell's contract covered the launching of the ship, as well as the building of it, and a dispute began to arise about the method to be used for launching. The origins of the conflict between Brunel and Scott Russell were to be found in an article in the *Observer* in November 1854. The great ship was a splendid source of copy for newspapers and magazines, for indeed nothing like it for scale or complexity had even been seen before, even in mid-nineteenth century England, which had seen so many impossibilities become fact that readers might have been excused for being rather blasé about another one. The *Observer* article was clearly written by someone very close to the centre of events, yet it mentioned Brunel only once, saying merely that as engineer he 'approved of the project, and Mr Scott Russell undertook to carry out the design'. Brunel was infuriated by this and by the errors in the article. He wrote a long letter on the subject to Yates, secretary of the Eastern Steam Navigation Co., and another very revealing letter to Scott Russell himself:

My dear Sir,
I have actually read through twice, the long article in the *Observer* and little as I generally regard newspaper notices I am amazed by it and, inasmuch as it has the *appearance* of authority particularly as I under-stand copies of it have been circulated by Mr. Yates which will give it the character of authenticity, I want to take some means of correcting or altering the impressions that might be produced by it – but before determining either whether I shall do so or how, I want to know its origin and whether it is (it does not look so) by a friendly hand who would himself rectify what I consider the errors of it, and I have written to Yates to learn. Cannot you help also to learn this?

The tone of the letter, giving Scott Russell a chance to make amends, shows fairly clearly that Brunel knew who was the source of the article.

By the beginning of 1855, these conflicts were overshadowed by the fact that despite his previous experience and not inconsiderable reputation as a shipbuilder, Scott Russell was in financial difficulties. This made the method of launching of vital pecuniary interest to him, and made it very hard to approach the matter in an objective manner, quite apart from his possible professional jealousy of Brunel. Russell wanted a free launch, with 12,000 tons sliding down the slipways into the Thames; Brunel regarded this as an invitation to catastrophe and wished to push the ship to the ends of the ways at low water, so that she could float off on the rising tide. The dispute was settled, after a growing lack of reasonable co-operation on Russell's part, by his financial failure in February 1856. Brunel had gradually lost faith in him, as repeated offers of assistance, warnings of danger, and requests for information, had produced no response. In fact Scott Russell had received all but £25,000 of his portion of the contract money, but when he gave up it was unhappily found by the E.S.N.Co. that roundly three quarters of the work for which he had been paid still remained to be done. He repudiated his contract, not having even paid his suppliers for much of the materials, and had no assets against which the steamship company could claim. There was no alternative, therefore, but to carry on with the work themselves, paying exhorbitant rent to the mortgagees of Russell's yard on which part of the ship stood, and exhorbitant wages to Russell's men, who alone knew enough about the design to carry it on. It was nearly June 1856 before they could restart work.

Brunel was not beaten by this setback, although he had no longer the resilience of youth and health to ride easily over it. His dogged determination was only increased, though the darkness was a little lightened by the way friends like Robert Stephenson, Gooch, and Capt. Claxton rallied round him, and the way his directors kept their faith in him, and did not give way to despair. Indeed, progress quickened, despite opposition from Russell as well as his mortgagee, which produced a most unhappy atmosphere on the site with everybody suspicious of everybody else. However, by September 1857 enough had been done to bring to the front the question of how to get the ship on her cradles down to the water.

Brunel's original plan was to push the cradles upon which the ship rested right down the ways with hydraulic presses. He abandoned this idea owing to its cost, and because of a conviction based on calculation that, once started down the slope by the presses, only a little pulling force might be needed to keep her moving; indeed, it might prove necessary to check too rapid movement. So the cradles were to be started off by hydraulic presses on the shore side, and the ship would then be pulled down to the water by chains rove through sheaves on barges and moorings in the river, back to steam-winches in the shipyard. Just as with the floating of the first truss at Saltash, the secret of success was to be meticulous planning, detailed rehearsals, and perfect order and quiet on the great day.

Alas for good intentions! The mortgagees of the yard were pressing the Eastern Steam Navigation Co. hard to give up possession, and Brunel had to agree reluctantly to try to launch the ship on 3 November 1857 before he was ready, without testing the moorings in the river, and without any detailed rehearsals. To crown it all the directors decided without telling him to raise some money by selling tickets of admission to the yard. Brunel was so harassed by these events that, asked to choose one from a list of possible names for the ship, he replied that they might call it *Tom Thumb* for all he cared. Nevertheless, a first attempt at launching was made just after noon, and, amid much pushing and pulling, the ship on her cradles began to move sidelong down the launching-ways. This caught by surprise the men at the drums of one of the great chains which were to check the movement if it became too fast, and some of them were injured, one fatally. The ship stopped. While she had been moving, the crews of the barges out in the river had panicked, and it was decided to dispense with them, and to rely on the hauling tackle at bow and stern, and the hydraulic presses. Brunel had another try at 2.00 p.m., but this time the moorings of the hauling-chains – never properly tested – began to drag, and work had to be suspended.

By the middle of November they were ready to try again. The river moorings were obviously almost useless, so more and bigger hydraulic presses were brought in, and on 19 November the great ship was moved a little nearer the water. The presses, however, had a stroke of only a few feet, and without sufficient reliable river tackle, the ship could be moved only in repeated short slips. The presses themselves were being worked to their limit, and there were frequent failures. It was observed that they 'perspired' freely, showing that the water under full pressure was being forced right through the too-porous cast iron. Although some progress was made, a combination of these mechanical troubles and the weather forced Brunel to allow the December high tide to come and go without touching the ship, but by the middle of January 1858 each high tide was taking some of her weight. Brunel was now virtually living in the yard, and at the end of January the cradles were off the end of the launching-ways, the hydraulic presses were taken away, and the final act depended on the high spring tide of Saturday, 30 January. Water was pumped into the double bottom to prevent the ship from floating until water level was high enough. The daylight tide of that day was too low, but the next day exceeded all expectations and, on 31 January 1858, the great ship floated free at last to her fitting-out berth across the river. She had been named *Leviathan* on that fateful November day in the previous year, but to all the world Brunel's third ship was the *Great Eastern,* and as such she was registered. Of all the congratulations he received, Brunel probably valued none more than those from Robert Stephenson, who had supported him like a true friend during the whole wearisome business, although his health was failing.

Stephenson was not the only one in poor health. Years of driving himself too hard had undermined even Brunel's iron constitution. Although he might well have eased up a little after the early success of the GWR, his letter-books indicate that even in his forties, he was as busy as ever, right up to the beginning of the *Great Eastern* affair. In 1850, when he was forty-four, he was asked by the Dean of Bristol to examine the tower of the cathedral which seemed to be in danger of collapsing. His reply was that for the next fortnight he would not be able to spare the time, but if someone with the keys and a ladder would meet him at the cathedral on a certain day at 5 a.m. he would have a couple of hours to do his inspection before catching the 7.50 train. All credit to him, the Dean turned out in person! As some slight concession to his advancing years, Brunel now travelled inside on stage coaches but an assistant who claimed the 'inside' fare on his expenses, when in fact he had travelled outside, earned the rebuke that 'when practicable you *should* travel outside; inside is by day – in England – only fit for women and invalids.' Now, after a winter of unrelieved anxiety on the Isle of Dogs, in the cold, and the fogs and the damp atmosphere of the Thames, he looked back on those days of a few years earlier, as a time of youthful health and vigour. After the launch, he was prevailed on to spend the summer of 1858 on the Continent, mainly in Switzerland. When he came back in September, his doctors promptly forbade another winter in England, and he was packed off to Egypt with Mary and Henry Marc. They had Christmas dinner in Cairo with Robert Stephenson, the last meeting between the two great engineers. The early part of 1859 was spent sailing up the Nile to the second cataract, and, when they returned to England in May, Brunel's health was somewhat restored.

The Eastern Steam Navigation Co. had, however, succumbed to the drain on its finances caused by the relentless demands of Scott Russell's creditors and mortgagees. A new company, the Great Ship Company, was formed to acquire the hull and to raise further funds. As Brunel had not only invested a large part of his personal fortune in the venture, but had also introduced many other large shareholders to the project, this capital loss affected him deeply. By the autumn of 1858 they had enough money to start the fitting-out, and, on the very day Brunel left for Egypt, the tenders came in. Amazingly there was one from Scott Russell, and, more amazing still, the directors accepted it in Brunel's absence, and despite an urgent letter from him, written at Lyons, warning them above all else to make sure that what they signed was an agreed and closely detailed specification. Scott Russell's tender was the very opposite. This unprincipled man had escaped legal bankruptcy by having instead a scheme of arrangement with his creditors, and by playing his cards carefully, he was able to use the funds which he had got from the E.S.N. Co. and concealed from his creditors, to rebuild his business.

Brunel therefore was faced by the worst possible situation on his return from Egypt: funds running out, and Scott Russell cheerfully playing fast and loose with the directors of the Great Ship Co., unbothered by any thoughts of financial obligations and unfettered by any detailed contract. Brunel plunged in, his health sinking fast, but driven on as in a dream, determined to get the ship ready for sea despite Scott Russell. His family, his friends, his doctors – among them Sir Benjamin Brodie and Dr. Richard Bright who gave his name to the disease from which his distinguished patient was suffering – urged him to rest, but this

was the last great adventure, the last struggle, and Brunel knew
it. Like an exhausted runner he pounded on, past the limit of
endurance and driven only by the spirit, running a race which
could end onl·· in collapse or victory.

On 6 September 1859, the *Great Eastern* was to move down the
Thames, adjust compasses, and sail for Weymouth, and Brunel
had chosen his cabin. He paid a last visit the day before, still
checking details (he had even selected the books for the ship's
library), and he posed for a photographer in front of one of the
five funnels. Suddenly, he collapsed and was carried ashore
partly paralysed, back to his home in Duke Street, the scene of so
much happiness and triumph. He rallied a little, and dictated a
few letters to Bennett. But his mind was with the *Great Eastern*,
and she was at sea.

It will be remembered that the essential point of the *Great
Eastern*'s design had been her great size as the way of reducing
coal consumption per ton of cargo carried. To assist this aim, she
was equipped with heaters for the boiler feed-water, in the shape
of iron water-jackets round the boiler flues which led to each
funnel. Water for the boiler was pumped into these jackets and
the flue gases warmed it before it was forced into the low-pressure
boilers either by pump or by gravity. Each jacket had an open
standpipe on top running up behind the funnel, to carry away
any steam that might be formed. Where the flues passed through
the Grand Saloon, the jackets served to insulate the passenger
accommodation from their heat, and vast mirrors concealed
them amid the ornate grandeur of this part of the ship. To make
sure the jackets did not leak, the standpipes behind the funnels
had been temporarily fitted with stopcocks, and then tested
hydraulically to 55 lb. of pressure.

Scott Russell's paddle-engines were under his overall control
on the trial trip, and one of his men was in charge of the auxiliary
machinery in the paddle engine-room. This was because the
engines had not then been given a satisfactory trial and the Great
Ship Co. had not accepted them from Scott Russell. As the *Great
Eastern* made her stately way down the English Channel, the dirt
left in the boilers from the Thames water caused them to prime,
and reduced the power of the pumps which forced sea-water into
the feed-water-jackets. To keep up the level of water in the
boilers, these pumps were turned from feeding the jackets to
feeding the boilers direct with cold water. The temporary stop-

cocks on the standpipes were, however, still in place, and they were closed. No longer fed with cold water from the sea, and unable either to communicate with the boilers below or the open air above, the jackets were thus changed into involuntary boilers. Off Hastings, the one round the forward funnel uptake burst with great force, fatally injuring several firemen. One of Scott Russell's men, realizing what had caused the explosion, hastily opened the corresponding stopcock on the jacket round the next funnel, and steam rushed out, showing that another explosion had been imminent. The paddle boiler-room was a shambles, but the ship steamed on, for the screw-engine boiler-rooms were able to supply the paddle-engines as well as their own. Without doubt the ship was saved by the great strength she derived from the cellular principle of construction.

We do not know whether the news of the explosion which would have been mortal to any other ship reached Duke Street from Hastings or from Weymouth, the *Great Eastern*'s first port of call. It has been said that the news killed Brunel, but, as he was already dying, worn out by his exertions on the ship, it certainly could do little more than take away the spirit upon which alone he had been living. Crushed, not by failure but by an absence of triumph, he died in the evening of 15 September 1859, six days after the explosion. And so the office where so many great schemes were born was silent at last.

12   A Man of his Time

Two days after the melancholy event, *The Times* printed a notice of Brunel's death, and two days later, a long obituary. At certain periods during the lifetime both of Isambard and his father, *The Times* had reported their achievements unfavourably, especially during the struggles with water in the tunnel beneath the Thames, and with the *Great Eastern* beside it. The obituary was happily a straightforward celebration of the man and his achievements, and the rancour of the past was forgotten. The next day, on 20 September, Isambard's body was taken to lie beside his father and mother in Kensal Green Cemetery in North London, the funeral procession being attended by many hundreds of friends and a large detachment from the GWR.

His family and friends commissioned a statue by Marochetti, which now stands in the Embankment Gardens, and a stained-glass window by Norman Shaw for Westminster Abbey. Today the window looks down on the graves of Telford, and Robert Stephenson who survived Brunel for less than a month. At a meeting of the Institution of Civil Engineers three weeks later, Joseph Locke, the third of the great railway engineers, said that the Institution had a duty to perform, to honour their memory and emulate their example, but he too was dead within a year. It was therefore left to others in the civil engineering world to erect a monument to which even Brunel would probably not have objected and, in 1860, Hawkshaw, Barlow, Claxton, and others formed a company for completing the Clifton suspension bridge. Although the original iron chains had been used as part of the Royal Albert Bridge at Saltash, other chains, which had been made for Brunel's Hungerford suspension bridge across the Thames, were used, that structure having been demolished to make way for the extension of the South Eastern Railway to their new Charing Cross station on the north bank of the river. The Clifton Bridge was at last opened on 8 December 1864, and, although it is not quite to Brunel's design in its engineering nor in his Egyptian style, it is probably close enough for the ghost of its designer to approve. One detail of the design, the decoration of the towers with cast iron panels depicting all the processes of making the materials and the bridge – starting with old Alderman Vick making his will in the 1750s – was not incorporated; happily, perhaps, because they would almost certainly have detracted from the simplicity of the towers which is so in tune with the plain and graceful leap of the span across the gorge.

It may be appropriate here to catalogue briefly what has happened to the rest of Brunel's major works. The *Great Eastern* was too big for her time; she even overwhelmed the firm who were breaking her up in the early 1890s, but not before she had found a place in history by laying the first successful transatlantic telegraph cable, under the guiding hand of Daniel Gooch who had retired – temporarily as it turned out – from the GWR. The great ship laid many other cables, round the world, before she was broken up at Birkenhead. The broad gauge was finally replaced in 1892 by the narrow gauge, though Daniel Gooch failed by three years to live to see that saddening event. Virtually all the main line railways of Brunel's creation still carry trains, though some of the branches have been closed. The timber viaducts were all replaced by the 1930s, and in the 1960s the Wye bridge at Chepstow was also replaced. Not so its mighty descendent at Saltash, which looks good for another century at least. Its designer, however, was never called on to bridge the River Severn, as seemed possible at one time, for his sketchbook for 20 April 1857 includes an outline design for the Severn, and the note: 'Q. Severn Bridge, is 1,100 ft. practicable?' The drawing shows a twin of the Saltash Bridge with two main trusses each twice the length of Saltash, and four times the section. It was never built, but what a bridge it would have been!

This story of so much high endeavour, and so much great achievement, would be incomplete without some attempt to assess Brunel's place in his own time, and in the wider sweep of an eventful century. In some ways, indeed, he was fortunate, because the pace of change in England in the first half of the nineteenth century was faster than ever before, and so a man who could imagine projects on a gigantic scale found his countrymen ready to listen. He was not alone in that, but he was spared the frustration experienced by a man like William James, who conceived a network of railways on a national scale, but a generation too early, and found that the world could not share his vision, and refused to make it fact. Yet, while Englishmen came to accept Brunel's conceptions of what a railway or a steamship should be, because they were rapidly becoming convinced that nothing indeed was impossible, he was often frustrated between conception and achievement by a shortage of money. Shortage in this sense is, of course, a relative term, for there was a shortage only because the costs of the projects were prone to exceed Brunel's estimates. Any attempt to find a recurring reason for this damaging flaw in the man's reputation is difficult. Certainly we cannot point to any carelessness in preparing the figures, or lack of attention to detail, yet the defect seemed to contemporaries to be persistent, perhaps because when Brunel built something – such as one of his later railways – where the estimates were *not* exceeded, the fact passed unnoticed. When, however, he struck out into fresh ground, as with the *Great Eastern,* and the excesses began to appear, probably due to novelty of the project, people forgot the times when he had been right. In his diary Daniel Gooch gives the best summing-up on this point.

By his death the greatest of England's engineers was lost, the man of the greatest originality of thought and power of execution, bold in his plans, but right. The commercial world thought him extravagant; but although he was so, great things are not done by those who sit down and count the cost of every thought and act.

So, in time, the narrow gauge came to make the broad gauge seem extravagant. In contrast, those who thought the *Great Western* and the *Great Britain* extravagant soon changed their views, because those ships set a standard which competitors had to meet by improving themselves, although it was Brunel's ill luck that the companies that owned the ships were not financially strong enough to build on their success. Of all Brunel's works, only the bridges escaped the charge of extravagance; a big bridge either stands or falls, and there is little room for argument about whether it does so extravagantly or not. When we look at the nineteenth century as a whole, as his contemporaries could not, doubts about Brunel's soundness as an engineer are greatly reduced, though even the most ardent admirer would have to agree that he sometimes made expensive mistakes in mechanical engineering. Interestingly, when the furore over the atmospheric system was at its height, Brunel was rejecting galvanism (electricity) as a motive power even of the near future, because he could appreciate how much greater than his problems were those to be overcome in making it more than an interesting toy.

Looking at Brunel as a professional man, rather than at his achievements, it is clear that he was very much of his times. He regarded his staff, from the senior assistant down to the office boy, as personal to himself. He held them to be dismissable at his pleasure; but we must not ignore that on the other hand he constantly tried to help and encourage them to better themselves. The offender was given many chances until he was proved incorrigible; the deserving were given a hand up the ladder of success by a good reference; and even the fallen were not ignored. As an example of this, he wrote to an assistant who was having difficulty with a contractor who had taken on more than he could manage: 'Poor Green; I dare say in the course of your travels you may hear me ridiculed, and as I wish people to be tender with me, I exhort you to be so with others like poor Green.' As a last instance of his reluctance to condemn those who had failed, there is a series of letters to Gravatt, whom he first met during his time in the Thames tunnel. Gravatt did the survey for the Bristol & Exeter line, and was in charge of some of the GWR works at the Bristol end where, due to his lack of care, some major errors were made; but Brunel gave Gravatt every chance to resign gracefully, writing letter after letter to persuade him to go before he had to tell the directors what had happened, which would leave them no alternative but dismissal. It would have been so easy just to have thrown Gravatt overboard; but that was not Brunel's way.

As the years went by, it is noticeable how railway projects became increasingly the field of the professional speculator – surveyors, contractors, and lawyers. Brunel started when railways were often less speculative, and public (rather than private) gain was more important. The position of the professional engineer changed as businessmen took over the lead from landowners, and Brunel became less of a moving spirit, and more one who just carried through the schemes of others. He certainly felt a growing disenchantment with those in control as he saw how different were the standards of business ethics and conduct. This did not prevent him in the early 1850s from devoting a great deal of time to restoring good relations between the GWR and the

South Wales Railway, although his attempts to reconcile the GWR with the Oxford, Worcester, & Wolverhampton Railway did not succeed, mainly because on the O.W. & W.R. side the will was lacking, whatever they said in public.

In private practice, separate from his GWR and associated interests, he was always pressed for time, and this caused him to refuse to have anything to do with promoters and inventors who wrote to him in great numbers to solicit his opinion and the support of his name. Yet in what he called 'this press of business', he would never refuse to help an old friend in trouble, and during the last years of his life, amid the sore trials of the *Great Eastern,* he was the moving spirit in attempts to restore the fortunes of a vicar at Torquay near his estate at Watcombe, who had bankrupted himself by expensive additions to his church. He was always very busy, but never too busy to help those in real need. And, although his business letters are mostly quite formal, even in them his sense of humour breaks through occasionally to give us a glimpse of what a desirable companion he must have been when he was not chained to his work.

His letters also give us a glimpse of the way in which the leaders of the fast-changing technology formed a small circle, freely drawing on one another for advice and information despite the public quarrels and opposing interests of their clients. There are many letters both inquiring for and giving information to others, but from them one quotation must suffice. He wrote to Michael Faraday, the pioneer of electricity, inquiring on some point, and started the letter by apologizing for 'troubling you with enquiries, but good nature is *always* abused, and therefore you cannot hope to escape'.

The vast volume of his work, and his unfailing insistence on always doing it in a methodical way and in minute detail, left him little time for involvement in some of the great events of his time, outside those of engineering and transport. It was a custom of the times for prominent men such as he to enter Parliament. Both Robert Stephenson and Locke did so, but when he was approached in 1847 to be a candidate for the Cricklade division (which then included Swindon and which Daniel Gooch represented from 1865 to 1885 without once speaking a word in the House of Commons) Brunel replied: 'I have neither time nor any desire to be in Parliament.' Brunel lived in a period when the ranks of that small circle whose influence and power controlled public policy in England were augmented by people who had risen in the world in a new way: they were industrial manufacturers, and men who made a living by the professions in the new science and technology. Change and novelty was the essence of their daily life, and their contribution to their times, so it is not surprising that in politics they tended to be found outside the ranks of the conservatives. In recommending an acquaintance to influential electors at Falmouth in 1851, Brunel spoke of his own position in an aside: 'I am a Whig, or something more.' That is virtually all we know of his political opinions, although, as one would expect, he was on the side of law and order at all times, as at Bristol in 1831, and at Westminster during the Chartist troubles in 1848. Of his attitude to some of the great political events of his time, such as the repeal of the Corn Laws and the coming of Free Trade, we have virtually no evidence beyond that of his admission of being something more than a Whig.

Prominent among the canons of those who did not shrink from change was faith in the virtues of competition, and uncompromising opposition to interference by the government. We know how Brunel followed this line during the gauge controversy. Competition would give the fruits of success to those who served their customers best, and would either extinguish the inferior, or make it improve to stay in the race. But in spite of this idea, under the constant urging of men like Edwin Chadwick, government did begin to take an interest: to interfere, as those staunch believers in 'the competitive principle' would have put it. The result was legislation about conditions of work, and the growth of the government inspectorate to see that the law was observed. On similar grounds – that competition would stimulate improvement and bring forward the best – Brunel was a lifelong opponent of the Patent Laws. On one occasion when they were under review, he put forward the suggestion that it should be made extremely easy to obtain a patent. This, he reckoned, would lead to such a rush that within six months anybody who wanted to develop some improvement would find his way blocked by a patent, and this in turn would cause an outcry which would lead to the end of the Patent Laws forever. The point which he failed to see was that sometimes it is necessary to have the financial rewards of an improvement reserved to the improver, because only thus could he hope to get financial backing for the researches in the first place.

In 1846 a paper of Chadwick's was read to the Statistical Society of Manchester, and in it the author urged legislation to place the responsibility on the railway companies for controlling and caring for the labour force of 'navvies'. To make the railway companies more careful of the men than the contractors were, Chadwick suggested that the men should have the right to compensation from their employers for any injuries sustained at work. The paper led to the appointment of a Select Committee of the House of Commons 'on the Condition of the Labourers employed in the Construction of Railways', and Brunel gave evidence before it. Chadwick also sent out copies of his paper to prominent men, Brunel among them.

In reply, Brunel pointed out that Chadwick seemed to ignore the fact 'that many of those who point to the evils in the system fall into the error of supposing that parties connected with the grievances, and the opportunities of profiting by them, do not anxiously endeavour to remedy them.' Brunel also feared that attempts for redress of these evils would only aggravate them. He continued:

'The most active of the prime causes susceptible to remedy are:

(1) The Truck[1] system, when abused as it generally is; I defy you to reach it by any law that a child cannot evade.

(2) Irregularity in the payments to men, which aggravates the evils of the Truck system.

(3) Subletting[2] to excess, especially among the smaller men where the subcontractors are only labourers of no resources or responsibility.

'This system leads to unsettled, roving, and reckless habits. If the subcontractor turns out bad the ganger [foreman] decamps, defrauding the men, and teaching them to be rascals in their turn. These evils may be reduced to nothing by encouraging responsible, respectable contractors, but you will not encourage them by making them legally

1. Under the Truck system the men were paid, not in money but in tickets which they could only exchange at a particular shop ('Tommy shop'), often owned by the contractor, where all too often prices were high and quality was low. The contractors originally were obliged, because of the isolation of their works from ordinary towns and villages, to provide such shops where the men could buy food and other necessaries. By exploiting a 'captive' market among the 'navvies' the unscrupulous contractor often turned this necessity into a profit.

2. The practice whereby the contractor for a length of the line would in his turn divide the work into contracts both smaller in length and more specialized in nature, so that one member of a gang of 'navvies' under a subcontractor would engage on behalf of the gang to do all the earth-moving needed over a short stretch.

responsible for the effects of a really accidental occurrence, any more than a manufacturer or the Marquis of Londonderry or any other mineowner. You drive them to evasions, and if they have responsibility for [navvies'] dependents, they will conceal accidents.'

In place of government regulations, with laws and inspectors, Brunel suggested a corresponding association of the leading engineers, contractors and railway companies, 'who would each in their respective spheres endeavour gradually to introduce improvements, and to this end should consult and assist each other.'

Whether such a loose association would have succeeded in making any effective improvements we shall never know, but it is a fact that great contractors like Brassey, who acted with fairness and regard towards their men, did not drive out of existence those of the opposite kind. By and large, the experience of the first half of the nineteenth century in many fields suggests that the believers in the competitive principle and non-interference by government were somewhat naïve, because the improvement in conditions only became noticeable once the inspectorate got to work. One of Brunel's commoner mistakes was expecting to find in others his own high standards. Unfortunately, perhaps because railway interests were so heavily represented in Parliament, nothing was done. The casual and shifting nature of the work, of course, made the forming of a Trade Union among the navvies virtually impossible.

We have no evidence of Brunel's attitude to unions, but although his general attitude was liberal, his strongly paternalistic view of his own staff suggests he would not have had much sympathy with them, expecting the faithful service of the servant to be justly rewarded by the liberality of the master without the need for organizations of workmen, or the intervention of paid negotiators on their behalf. That he was concerned with the greater well-being of the labouring classes is shown by the lengthy and sometimes ponderous praise which he as Reporter on the Buildings Section of the Great Exhibition, used to commend the model dwellings for the working classes, which were sponsored by Prince Albert. Brunel is sure, in his report, that this improved class of building would appeal by its merit, and be speedily adopted. In this, alas, he took too sanguine a view of the qualities valued by builders for the masses, and the new slums continued to be built despite the existence of something better. The model cottages are still with us, on Kennington Common, where they were re-erected after the Great Exhibition [Plate 21].

Although genius is, among many other quotations, 'an infinite capacity for taking pains', and that certainly is characteristic of all of Brunel's work, I hesitate to apply it to Isambard Brunel. In reserving it for a man like Leonardo da Vinci, it becomes necessary to supply some description in its place. That Brunel was a great innovator in several aspects of communication by land and sea is not open to doubt, and it is scarcely worthwhile to try to assess whether it was in railways, bridges, or ships, that his contribution was the most original, or the most useful. I come, at this last, to the conclusion that for him the solution of the problem was often the greater attraction. In the course of solving so many, he undoubtedly established himself in the eyes of the world as he longed to do. So often the technical problem led to an organizational problem, the task of carrying through what he had started. 'When I have formed a decided opinion no fear of the consequences ever prevents my expressing it,' he once said. Having put his hand to a task, his spirit would not let him give it up uncompleted. Perhaps at some time he came upon the prayer of that other great pioneer of the seas, Sir Francis Drake, whose words are so appropriate to Brunel:

'O Lord when thou givest to thy servants to endeavour in any great matter, grant us to know that it is not the beginning but the continuing of the same until it be thoroughly finished, that yieldeth the true glory.'

Bibliography

BEAMISH, Richard, *Memoir of the life of Sir Marc Isambard Brunel* (Longman, Green, Longman & Roberts, London, 1862).

BRUNEL, Isambard, *The Life of Isambard Kingdom Brunel, Civil Engineer* (Longmans Green, London, 1870).

CLEMENTS, Paul, *Marc Isambard Brunel* (Longmans Green, London, 1970).

GIBBS, G. H., *Extracts from the Diaries of (GWR Magazine,* London, 1909–10). Reprinted by Adams & Dart, Bath, 1971.

GOOCH, Sir Daniel, *The Diaries of* (Paul, Trench & Trubner, London, n.d.). Reprinted by David & Charles, Newton Abbot, 1972.

Great Exhibition of 1851: Report of the Jury on Buildings (London, 1851).

HADFIELD, Charles, *Atmospheric Railways* (David & Charles, Newton Abbot, 1967).

HORSLEY, J. C., *Recollections of a Royal Academician* (John Murray, London, 1903).

LATIMER, John, *Annals of Bristol* (W. & F. Morgan, Bristol, 1887).

MACDERMOTT, E. T., *History of the Great Western Railway* (GWR, London, 1927–31).

MACFARLANE, Charles, *Reminiscences of a Literary Life* (John Murray, London, 1903).

MOSES, E. Watts, *The Williamsons of East Markham* (Sunderland,n.d.)

NOBLE, Lady Celia Brunel, *The Brunels, Father and Son* (Cobden-Sanderson, London, 1938).

ROLT, L. T. C., *Isambard Kingdom Brunel* (Longmans Green & Co., London, 1957).

ROWLAND, K. T., *The Great Britain* (David & Charles, Newton Abbot, 1971).

Other sources of information:

Archives of the Great Western Railway, in the Public Record Office, Kew.

The Brunel Room, Great Western Railway Museum, Swindon.

House of Lords Library, London.

Newspaper archives of: *The Times; Illustrated London News; Illustrated Times.*

Index